THE TREASURE HUNT BOOK

THE TREASURE HUNT BOOK

Candida Geddes · Peter Arnold · Patricia Pierce

Foreword by
Anneka Rice

Hamlyn

Maps © copyright MICHELIN et Cie 1985.
Based upon Ordnance Survey Maps with the permission of the Controller
of H. M. Stationery Office. Crown copyright reserved.

Published by The Hamlyn Publishing Group,
Bridge House, 69 London Road,
Twickenham, Middlesex TW1 3SB,
and distributed for them by
Hamlyn Distribution Services Limited,
Rushden, Northants, England NN10 9RZ.

© Copyright The Hamlyn Publishing Group, 1986

First published 1986
ISBN 0 600 55073 7

Printed and bound by Graficromo s.a., Cordoba, Spain

Contents

Foreword
by Anneka Rice

*Everyone I meet imagines that I spend my life
rushing around in a brightly coloured
jumpsuit, with earphones on – a helicopter
ticking over in the back garden. The truth is,
the whole extraordinary Treasure Hunt ritual
takes up only one month of my time each year.*

*The filming of Treasure Hunt conjures up
all sorts of wonderful memories – helicopters
landing on manicured lawns, rounders on the
beach, tea and croquet, Frankie smelling of
Deep Heat ointment, camaraderie and, above
all, the kind of relentless good-humoured
teasing that only occurs among a group of
people who've worked closely together for
several years. The Treasure Hunt Book will
enable you to share those precious four weeks
with us, so that when you see the programmes
on television you will feel that you know each
member of the 'team', even the ones behind
the scenes. Then there are the ten 'Armchair
Treasure Hunts', which we invite you to play.
Have fun.*

*People seem to watch Treasure Hunt for
different reasons. For some, it is the
excitement of solving the clues before the
contestants; for others it is the glorious
countryside, and the stunning aerial
photography. For us the Treasure Hunt team,
the most important part of the programme is
you, the audience.*

*I am constantly amazed and touched by
your letters – I've never worked on a series
that inspires so much loyalty among its
viewers: I recognise some of the names and
handwriting from our first series. As long as
you keep watching, we'll keep running. Who
knows, in 2010 Graham, Frankie and I may be
charging around in motorised bathchairs.*

Anneka Rice

The Making of Treasure Hunt

'Hallo, and welcome to this week's Treasure Hunt.'

At these words, millions of Channel Four viewers sharpen their wits, hands poised over reference books, in their weekly attempt to prove that if only *they* were in the studio, they would direct the lovely Anneka Rice, *Treasure Hunt*'s famous skyrunner, accurately and speedily towards the treasure. Millions more people sit back to have the dark winter evening brightened by spectacular aerial views of some of Britain's loveliest countryside, filmed in an apparently endless sunny summer climate, and cheered by the equally sunny personality of the skyrunner.

So much more than just another TV quiz show, *Treasure Hunt* is television's most popular adventure game. The first episode of the first series attracted 900,000 viewers; half-way through the fourth series the ratings broke through the six million mark – an event that caused joy and jubilation (and a stampede to the fridge to get at a bottle of champagne) among the staff at Chatsworth Television, who make the programmes for Channel Four.

The idea behind the show is very simple. Two contestants in the studio are asked to solve between them five cryptic clues. Each clue leads the skyrunner, who acts as the contestants' eyes and legs on location, to find the next clue. There is a money prize for each clue solved, and if all five are solved and the skyrunner reaches the 'treasure' at the end of the course, they win £1,000. The clues are structured so that they can be deciphered by looking at a map of the area where the helicopter-borne skyrunner is located, and by using a selection of reference books on the studio shelves. The host of the show, Kenneth Kendall, and skyrunner, Anneka, have no prior knowledge of the location or the solutions to clues. Skyrunner and studio are linked by two-way radio, but that is their only form of communication – they cannot see each other, though the skyrunner's activities are filmed by a cameraman and recordist out on location. Anneka also has a map, and follows the instructions the contestants give her about where to go next, showing the helicopter pilot the direction of the next site and then, when she has been asked to land, running, rowing, abseiling or whatever is demanded of her to find precisely where the next clue, written on a small piece of pink card, is hidden.

Treasure Hunt may be simple in concept, but it is one of television's most complex programmes to produce. Watching the show, it is sometimes hard to remember that during filming there are only sound links between Anneka and the contestants, so her descriptions of what she can see both from the air and on the ground are an essential link in the clue-solving process. Communications, maintaining the sound between the skyrunner and the studio and all the other people involved (the skyrunner helicopter, the communications helicopter, the producer in the outside broadcast van), are technically difficult and constantly changing. Although pre-recorded, the programme is produced under live conditions, in continuous real time. This means that once the clock has been started it is not stopped – there are no retakes, no pauses for the contestants to change their minds, no going back and having another go if Anneka has to grab a moving clue and misses it. There is absolutely no cheating as far as the timing of the

programmes is concerned. The only time the clock is stopped is to allow for the two commercial breaks, and then the contestants are led away from the studio set so they can't do any illicit homework during the break in filming. The secrecy surrounding the locations chosen and the clues themselves is absolute. Anneka herself says that she 'feels like some kind of outcast – a leper' half the time on location, as the rest of the team, who know where the next day's filming is to take place, clam up whenever she appears. Similarly, in the studio Kenneth Kendall is kept completely in the dark until the table map is unrolled for the contestants at the beginning of each programme.

Twelve programmes filmed in the United Kingdom, and one overseas 'special', make up each series of *Treasure Hunt*. To prepare, film and edit the series takes the full year. The early stages, which begin in November, consist of choosing locations and organising a desired route, finding out the feasibility of landing sites for the helicopter, thinking of ever craftier places to hide clues and ever zanier antics for Anneka to undertake in pursuit of them. During this period the contestants are also selected: thirteen couples from among thousands of applicants. Locations are reconnoitred first from the ground and later from the air, and when the routes and events have been agreed the clues are written and the blown-up Ordnance Survey maps used in the studio can be ordered. Filming takes place during June and July, on location all over the country and in the studio at Limehouse Studios in London's dockland. For the director and her assistants, based in the studio during filming while the producer runs the location end, the hard work carries on after filming is completed: it takes five months to edit together the location and the studio videotapes, to marry in the sound and to finalise the film.

It seems a paradox, but the unique spontaneity and excitement of *Treasure Hunt* is possible only because of the months of careful planning and meticulous attention to detail that go into each programme. It became very evident while talking to the various people involved that everyone on the team is a star. Each person's work is really vital to the success of the programme as a whole. Without the creative guidance of both producers, Malcolm Heyworth and Peter Holmans, there would be no show. Without the champagne personality and sparkle of Anneka Rice, there would be no show. Without the inventiveness, careful research and planning of Jennifer Gradwell and Anne Evans, there would be no locations and no clues, and no show. Nor would there be a show without the administrative skills of Angela Breheny and Victoria Bartleet, who cope with the office and select the contestants; nor without the extraordinary skill and stamina of the location cameraman, Graham Berry, and his video engineer, Frank Meyburgh. Then, there is the talented flying of Keith Thompson and Michael Malric-Smith, the knob-twiddling expertise of Nigel Tilbury, who is in charge of communications, and all their helpers. Without contestants prepared to play the game, the host, Kenneth Kendall, and the adjudicator Wincey Willis, to keep them on the straight and narrow, the director, Chris Gage, the

◀ Peter Holmans, a director of Chatsworth Television and joint producer of *Treasure Hunt*.

▶ Malcolm Heyworth *Treasure Hunt* producer, resplendent in his specially knitted *Treasure Hunt* sweater.

production assistant, June Mason, and all the others involved in the studio, there would be no show. (And without the amazing amount of cooperation from all of them, there would have been no book.)

For those who work on *Treasure Hunt*, it is a unique show. The same response emerged whenever members of the team were asked what it was like to work on the programme – whether *Treasure Hunt* differed in any way from other television or film work. It is different: there is more fun, more flexibility, more trust, more individual responsibility; there is no room for primadonna behaviour and none appears, and they all get on together famously. The first thought is that this must just be showbiz talk, but it is impossible to crack the façade of it all being a happy family, a true team who love working together and look forward to filming from one year to the next.

'You never will crack it,' smiled Malcolm when he heard the author's complaint about the unanimous sweetness-and-light picture projected, 'because it is true.' If a programme is tightly scripted, if there is no possibility of the unexpected ever happening, if outsiders are not involved, it is probably possible to produce a good programme,

▲ Shooting the title sequence – helicopter pilots show their great skill in manoeuvring their machines.

even if the participants all detest each other. But the very closely knit team is perhaps the most important ingredient in the recipe for *Treasure Hunt*'s enormous success: they do all depend on each other and trust each other, and that is why it works.

What makes *Treasure Hunt* such good television entertainment from the audience's point of view? There is no single answer, and while the ratings go on rising and the people involved go on creating good new programmes, nobody is too bothered about analysing it. They are more interested in finding ways of improving the programme to make sure its success continues.

Treasure Hunt originated in France, where Jacques Antoine devised with TéléUnion a series which was called *Chasse au Trésor*. There were from the outset fundamental differences in approach and format between the French series and the more exciting game that the Chatsworth Television producers, Malcolm and Peter, wanted. For example, in *Chasse au Trésor* there was just one long clue and the skyrunner was male.

Malcolm and Peter eventually persuaded the French company that their modifications would be acceptable.

When *Treasure Hunt* was being planned, Malcolm Heyworth had already decided that he wanted a female skyrunner, and that personality was going to be as important as athletic prowess. So, as well as contacting well-known sporting figures, he also trawled the personality agencies. One of them came up with Anneka Rice, then little known in Britain, though she was a familiar face on Hong Kong television after several years there presenting a variety of programmes and, as a newsreader, with a much more serious image than she now has in Britain. As soon as she arrived for her interview, Malcolm thought Anneka was going to be right for the job, but to make sure he took six potential skyrunners to Hyde Park, together with his cameraman, Graham Berry, for a test run. Anneka recalls: 'The others all looked so

professional, limbering up in their sponsored training shoes, doing press-ups all over the place. I thought I didn't stand a chance.' But she did. At first Graham himself ran after the candidates, but after a couple of them showed him that he was even less fit than he had thought – by zooming off into the distance with never a backward glance in his direction – he resorted to a tripod and some rather long-distance filming. After her test run, Anneka overheard him say to Malcolm: 'It'll have to be Annie, she's the only one I'll be able to keep up with.' That was in fact not Malcolm's prime reason for selecting her. During her test Anneka ran into the Hyde Park police station, where her charm and enthusiasm persuaded a policeman to come out and help her find where the clue was hidden. This ability to talk to people, to infect them with her own eagerness, is one of Anneka's great strengths, and Malcolm knew for certain then that he had found what he was looking for. And he has been proved right. Everyone agrees that Annie's special kind of unselfconscious excitement, the fervour with which she searches

▲ **Anneka's favourite photograph of herself.**

for clues, her ability to make a fool of herself with perfect good humour and aplomb, the friendliness, jokes and laughter, make the show unique. You could not script such spontaneity, not even with a professional actress: it must be genuine. She is also an exceptionally attractive lady, not only as far as the adult male population is concerned, but also because she has a freshness ('wholesome' is a word that keeps cropping up when people describe her) that appeals to mothers, and children think she is wonderful.

Independent production companies in television have not only to think up good ideas for programmes but also to sell those ideas. When the idea for *Treasure Hunt* was first put forward, Channel Four had a new commissioning editor in Cecil Korer, who was to be enormously supportive during the programme's early days. He commissioned the first series of eleven programmes. The very first one was to take place at Luxor, in Egypt, in collaboration with the French, who agreed to be responsible for all the organisation for both teams. The British would choose their own course and do their own filming. It turned out to be a classic administrative nightmare. When the Egyptian helicopters landed at Luxor airport they were refused permission to carry external aerials (without which the sound could not be transmitted between location and studio); the head of antiquities at Luxor said that the helicopters could not land near the temples – they could take off and circle nearby, but not land! Days passed, with Malcolm sitting, increasingly hot and increasingly bothered, in various military chiefs' offices trying to unravel the problems. Not even the arrival of Anneka herself softened their hearts. The studio booking in London could not be rescheduled, so plans were made to fly Kenneth Kendall and the two contestants to Paris in the hope that the studio link-up could go ahead from there. But it was no good; the tangled web of Egyptian bureaucracy proved too much even for Malcolm's determination, and the show had to be abandoned. It was hardly an auspicious beginning. Cecil Korer was undaunted, and suggested that they should do a pilot show in England, at short notice, wherever they could. So the team took a deep breath, and with very little time available set up a London show that centred on Greenwich. This time they were on their own, without any help from the more experienced French team. Because the communications were innovative and had not been properly tested beforehand, there was chaos behind the scenes, but luck was on their

▲ The viewers are unaware of how close the camera's eye often is to Anneka's relaxed, smiling face.

side, the filming went fairly smoothly, and the producers felt that the show had worked. They held their breath as Cecil Korer telephoned his verdict. 'I'm very undecided,' he said – and their spirits sank. 'I can't quite make up my mind whether it is fantastic or brilliant.' Elation! And the series went ahead.

Since the first series there have been continuous improvements and modifications to the show. The studio set has been improved, the technical side (camerawork, sound recording, communications) has been radically altered. In the first series location filming started early in the morning because it was felt that the show would work better if not too many people were around. But Annie is at her best on the ground talking to people, so filming now takes place later in the morning, and as the programme has become better known the opposite problem is encountered: it is now difficult to keep the crowds down so that the helicopter can land safely and Annie's progress towards a clue is not impeded by hordes of onlookers. The later starts have also meant an easier life for the hotel managers on location; it was sometimes a little difficult for them to persuade other guests, who had gone to a comfortable country-house hotel for a quiet break, that they should enjoy the sound of helicopter motors starting up at seven in the morning!

Anneka Rice

The *Treasure Hunt* team may all be stars in their own right, but the others would agree that the star who shines the brightest is **Anneka Rice**. Her warmth and friendliness, enthusiasm and excitement are as evident off camera as during shooting. Everybody working on *Treasure Hunt* feels intensely loyal towards her. In the five years since the first programmes were made she has become really famous and instantly recognisable. She features in television awards ceremonies, is constantly in demand for public appearances; she is a major celebrity. And it seems not to have gone to her head at all. She is the first to tell you stories against herself, to recount the others' kindness and helpfulness, to emphasise that she doesn't get – and doesn't expect – star treatment on location. She does get the best room, but she deserves to, as she is confined to barracks while all the others are out doing the rehearsal run. And if she finds, as she sometimes does, a jacuzzi in her bathroom, she invites the others to use it – even though she may wait until one team member is safely ensconsed in steaming bubbles and then invite all the others to come and enjoy the spectacle. (And they got their own back. On another occasion, Annie practised her singing – for a pantomime role – while they were out on rehearsal, warbling away in her room with her practice tape turned up to full volume. During a pause in her efforts she heard a strange sound, and discovered the entire team standing outside the door listening to her.)

Anneka is a fitness fanatic, which is just as well, for her life generally is very demanding, and her role in *Treasure Hunt* particularly so. She has a fully equipped gymnasium in her house, plays tennis, runs, does weight-training, and is very careful about what she eats. She knows that she has to be in peak condition if she is to cope with all the demands the course-setters devise, and have enough puff left to talk at the same time. While *Treasure Hunt* is on location there is usually plenty of time for exercise. During rehearsals,

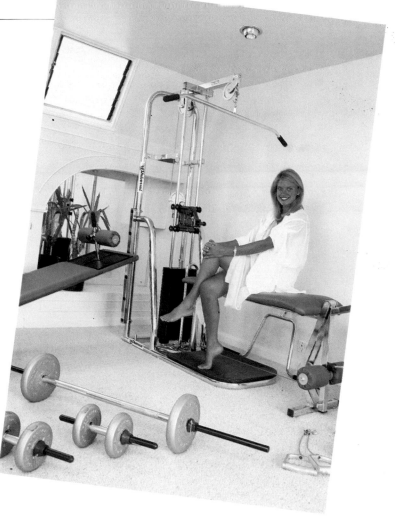

▲ Fitness is an essential part of the job. To help her stay at her peak in spite of her hectic life, Anneka has a fully equipped gymnasium on the top floor of her house.

when she is whiling away her time at the hotel, there is usually a swimming pool at her disposal. (To keep the whole team happy, jacuzzis, snooker tables and other sporting facilities are usually provided too.) When the day's filming is over there is often time for a companionable – though also competitive – jog with Graham and Frank, as though they didn't spend enough time running together against the clock!

Annie's favourite anecdote, to illustrate that she really doesn't get star treatment – and that the show goes on – describes her visit to Hickstead in Sussex. She had to run into the ring during a show-jumping competition. The marshals primed to guide her safely in the right direction didn't quite manage to do so, and she was cannoned into by a competing horse, which sent her flying, badly bruised and considerably shocked. The two questions she was asked on her headset as she lay for a moment, dazed and breathless, were: 'Is your

for the new series. 'He thought it would look good if I did a free-fall parachute jump. I pointed out that if I broke my leg I wouldn't be able to do the programmes. "Oh, don't worry," he said. "We would only film the sequence *after* we'd finished all the location filming." He wasn't a bit concerned about my leg!'

Some of the escapades devised for Annie in the course of tracking down clues do alarm even her just a little. When the 'special' in Florida was being filmed, she had to join a trapeze act. This

◄ Anneka returned to Florida's Sea World dolphinarium when the day's filming was over to play with this dolphin.

▲ Horses always go down well with the viewers, and Anneka has had several encounters with them, show-jumpers and police horses as well as this placid creature.

equipment all right?' and 'Has the horse been hurt?' She managed to finish the show, but was later taken to the hospital on the Isle of Wight. It was typical of Annie (who didn't tell this part of the story) that at the hospital, in spite of her own injuries, she spent nearly two hours sitting with a young lad who had been injured in a motorcycle accident, until his father arrived to look after him.

Annie is also amused by one of Malcolm's latest and greatest suggestions for an opening sequence

part of the course had been tested beforehand by Chris Gage, the director, who was 'volunteered' by Malcolm, his own substantial build considered by all to be unsuitable for such frolics. Malcolm was confident that it was safe, but Annie was far from happy as she was launched into space, even though she had been harnessed up and there was a safety net somewhere away below her. Occasionally even Malcolm thinks it might be wise for Annie to put in some practice; her abseiling

▼ At a Punch and Judy show,
Llandudno, North Wales.

▲ **One lucky child fulfilled a dream by joining Anneka in the helicopter on a *Jim'll Fix It* programme.**

lesson stood her in good stead when she had to find a clue half way down a German lookout tower in Guernsey, with nothing but a rope between her and eternity as she stood out 90° from its sheer wall. With experience, too, Annie has learned that when Malcolm first contacts her at the beginning of the year to discuss a new series, she should listen carefully for any hints he might drop about new activities it might be just as well to learn . . .

'Annie is magic – she is so natural.' 'Annie is now terribly good with maps.' 'Annie has impeccable manners – even in the midst of all the excitement she will remember to thank people who have helped her or apologise if she bumps into anybody.' 'Annie is such a loyal friend.' 'Annie is completely professional. She takes the work immensely seriously and never messes about or does a difficult megastar act.' There can be no media heroine who is spoken about with more affection by the people she works with.

The affection is mutual. 'When I first started working on *Treasure Hunt* I didn't have many friends in London,' Annie recalls. 'Now some of the team are my best friends, so it has been important to me personally, not only fantastic for my career.' For Annie the only price of success is being a famous and instantly recognisable face. She finds the loss of privacy hard to bear. 'I have become increasingly shy in public,' she admits, 'and really can't face doing something quite simple, like going shopping, on my own. People always mean to be friendly, but if you're in a hurry or the fiftieth person says, "Where's the helicopter, then, Annie?" it is sometimes difficult to respond as well as you should.' But she accepts that this is an unavoidable problem that goes with being such a popular television figure, and prefers to dwell more on what fun she has and how lucky she has been, than on the minor drawbacks of being public property.

Kenneth Kendall

Kenneth Kendall's face must be one of the most familiar on television, but after years of presenting serious information to the nation with a serious expression on his face, he is delighted to be involved in a programme as lively as *Treasure Hunt*. One of the problems about being a newsreader, apart from the fact that everyone expects you to be an expert on current affairs for the rest of your life, is that little personality or sense of humour is allowed to show through. Kenneth has both. It was a lucky chance that Kenneth is also dedicated to solving *The Times* crossword, and is therefore in his element helping contestants if he can. When Malcolm was considering whom to invite to act as host, he knew he wanted to find someone who had already made a name, who had arrived. 'I didn't want someone who still needed to get noticed. It is a vitally important support role, but we didn't want a host who would hog the limelight.' With his calm, soothing manner, his quiet persistence in solving the clues and his gentle redirection of contestants who are floundering, Kenneth is ideal for the task.

In spite of his relaxed air, Kenneth is working very hard. The show demands enormous concentration as there is so much going on at once. He is very aware of the importance of trying to make the contestants feel at ease, and tries hard to reduce the pre-show nerves from which they all suffer. He also plays a part in pacing the show: letting the contestants get on with clue-solving virtually unaided, or positively helping if they are not making much progress. 'We are always hoping that contestants will have as much personality as brain. The worst ones are those who constantly have their noses in books, and forget either to give Annie any instructions or to talk about what they are looking up.' He admits, though, that in the heat of the moment it can be difficult even for the experts to remember exactly what they should be doing. 'I get just as involved as the contestants in trying to solve the clues,' Kenneth reflects. 'Almost

▲ Kenneth Kendall, relaxed and affable, at his best putting contestants at their ease and helping them to enjoy the show.

every show we do I talk into the books, and the director has to remind me to turn round before I speak.'

Kenneth also admits that his appreciation of the contestants' position has grown since the awful day that the tables were turned, and he and Anneka were put in the role of contestants. Ned Sherrin acted as host, and there were three guest skyrunners, Wayne Sleep, Kenny Lynch and

21

► **Gemma Craven, Wayne Sleep and Kenny Lynch relax over a glass of champagne with Kenneth, Anneka and guest host Ned Sherrin after the special show.**

REFERENCE

Gemma Craven. There can be few people more accustomed to the tension of a studio, the lights, the feeling of an earpiece burbling away into your numbed brain. Nevertheless, for Kenneth the experience was 'absolutely terrifying. There was a terrible feeling of the minutes on the clock ticking away – the pressure was unbelievable. I used to feel a bit irritated with contestants sometimes when they simply didn't seem to be trying, but having been in their position myself I am now much more sympathetic.' Very occasionally the contestants become too lively even for Kenneth:

two dear ladies on one show wouldn't stop talking, and in the end Kenneth resorted to clapping a hand over their mouths!

One of Kenneth's tasks is to hold the show together if there are technical problems. The most common difficulty is with communications: if the contestants and Anneka can't hear each other clearly, everyone's job is made more difficult, and precious time is wasted if instructions and comments need to be repeated several times. It is almost impossible to imagine, when sitting at home watching the show, the difference there is when

you cannot see what is happening out on location. The contestants are effectively blind, and need to have Anneka's help in describing what she sees, so they can make informed guesses if their own sleuthing through the reference books isn't coming up with the right answer quickly enough; and she needs to have from them as much detailed information as possible about what to look out for. When 'comms' (communications) are bad, the pressure on contestants and skyrunner mounts. Somehow it isn't much help to know that Malcolm is out there somewhere in the communications van, mouthing desperately to Nigel, and that Nigel is talking equally frantically to the 'comms' helicopter trying to improve its position and get the sound to come through clearly. Even with so much experience behind them, the communications team sometimes find it very difficult to maintain clear sound links between Anneka and the studio, and it is a great help to the contestants to have Kenneth interpreting the muffled sounds for them, and repeating their requests to Anneka while they get on with puzzling out the clues. Everyone agrees that he is always a pleasure to work with.

◀ **Personalities in action: Kenny Lynch 'enjoys' a helicopter ride –**

▶ **– Gemma Craven talks to the studio team from the top of a tourist bus –**

◀ **– Wayne Sleep rushes off in hot pursuit of a clue**

Wincey Willis

Wincey Willis has added the role of adjudicator on *Treasure Hunt* to a working day that would already seem quite gruelling enough for most of us. For the past three and a half years her alarm clock has gone off at 3.15 a.m., five mornings a week. At 4.15 a.m. she is in the studio preparing for her appearance on TVam. While *Treasure Hunt* is being filmed, Wincey comes off the air in north London at 9.25 a.m., gallops into a taxi and speeds off to Limehouse Studios through the morning traffic. Shooting usually starts around 10.30, by which time Wincey has freshened up, might have had the chance to scald her throat by drinking a cup of coffee at excessive speed, and is in her place on the studio set looking all ready to start again. As she says, 'On *Treasure Hunt*, nobody is allowed to feel tired till I do.'

Wincey began her working life as a travel courier, then moved to radio. A colleague who made the change to television eventually asked her to do a one-off slot with animals (which are Wincey's great passion – she owns 64 different creatures). This brief exposure to the cameras happened to be seen by Muriel Young, who was head of children's programmes and was looking for someone to do animal items . . . so Wincey moved to television.

Wincey's sense of humour contributes a good deal to the fun in the studio, and helps to put the contestants at their ease. She is particularly anxious that they should not feel under pressure and believes that it is not their job to have to cope with technical problems as well as carrying responsibility for solving the clues. She will sometimes resort to daft effects to make contestants relax, though we may never know what one couple thought when at rehearsal she was sporting a different animal's nose every time they looked her way.

Her sense of humour goes down well with the studio cameramen, perhaps particularly when the joke is on someone else. Like Phil, for instance. He

▲ Wincey Willis, envy of contestants and viewers at the beginning of each programme, as she is the only one on the studio floor who knows all the answers.

operates the camera and takes shots of the big map used by the contestants. The camera is fixed high up on a gantry. At the beginning of each shoot, Phil climbs his ladder to the camera, and sits in splendid isolation – indefinitely, if nobody remembers to bring the ladder back again. 'Who's a pretty boy, then?' Wincey calls up to him. One day, in a specially mischievous mood, she produced a cuttlefish bone, a bell and mirror, and a spray of millet, and with the help of the props team arranged all this up in the rigging. When Phil climbed his ladder that day it was whisked away even faster than usual, special pink lights were trained on him, and there the budgie sat, high up in his unique cage, with plenty to keep him entertained – though flakes of millet did cause problems falling on to the maps for the next few days.

In spite of all the fooling around, Wincey takes her part in *Treasure Hunt* seriously. One of her reasons for enjoying working on the programme is that she has discovered, in common with many viewers, what an enormous number of beautiful and interesting places there are in Britain, and has been inspired to visit many of them herself. She has also acquired a good deal of information about the locations. Anne Evans, the clue writer, gives her notes about each location before the programme begins, so that Wincey has snippets to give the viewers if there is a lull in the conversation between Annie and the contestants, or if things are progressing so fast that a little time needs to be filled before the clock is restarted following a commercial break. At the same time as marking the route on her map, deciding when to fill in a gap and keeping abreast of progress, Wincey has three different voices in her ear: she can hear Anneka, the studio team, and is also wired to the control room so that she can be kept informed of the timings, which she passes on to contestants so they can check how they are getting on. Doing so many things at once has become no more difficult than driving a car for someone who has had five and a half years working with the pressures of live television.

◄ **After her dash across London from TVam to Limehouse Studios, Wincey catches her breath in make-up before going into the studio.**

Be prepared!

According to the *Treasure Hunt* calendar, the year starts in November for Anne Evans and Jenny Gradwell. Their work begins with thinking up new locations. First Jenny studies a master map to find gaps. It is preferable to go to areas where they have not been before that are also both photogenic and Jenny Gradwell go off together for an eight-week stint of hotel life on the first of the programme's 'recces'. They have a difficult and complicated job ahead of them. They have to imagine what an area will look like in summer, as they stand in freezing winds and a snow-clad

and interesting; she also contacts local tourist offices to obtain lists of special events that might be of interest. Anne approaches the problem by thinking first of places that she knows, as it makes her task of creating the clues at a later stage that much easier. By Christmas they have worked up the fifteen or so locations that they wish to explore.

In the early weeks of the new year Anne Evans

▲ Anne Evans, the clue writer, pursues the elusive clues by referring to a wide range of books as well as delving into her own prodigious memory. With Jenny Gradwell, researcher and location co-ordinator, she first goes on a two-month 'recce' of locations.

landscape. They must work out from the ground whether that patch of coastline, shrouded in thick mist, will look breathtaking from the air and will therefore be worth filming, or if the bare,

▲ Jenny Gradwell manages to keep smiling through all the chaos and crises.

► Malcolm and Jenny finalise plans for a show during the rehearsal.

►► No wonder Anneka is looking slightly alarmed: the vital clue is hidden beneath the skirts of this medieval fertility figure.

colourless outlines of a famous garden will really come alive in a blaze of colour to entrance viewers at the height of the flowering season. Establishing a good route, with varied locations, enough local interest, spectacular views and clue-worthy sites is not easy. Add to that the need for safe landing sites for the helicopter and the need to obtain cooperation and landing permission from the owners of each of the places they wish to visit, and you can begin to see how complex a business it all is. Jenny's and Anne's own inventiveness is called

upon, too: if a location is a bit short of drama, maybe some Red Devils could come parachuting in, or a cricket match be specially staged; if something special is happening nearby (a medieval fair, important local agricultural show, and so on) could it be incorporated into the filming schedule if the dates can be made to fit? With more experience comes more flexibility and the urge to find ever more outrageous exploits for Anneka. Each course is limited to about twenty-five miles, giving extra time to allow for special stunts, hitching lifts or whatever else the researchers can dream up as they plan each course. There are other niceties that have to be remembered, too. For example, from the cameraman's point of view it is best to fly from south to north, so the sun is behind the camera, but in Britain the most beautiful stretches of coastline are in the west; Graham has to sit on the left-hand side of the helicopter so he can film Anne rushing off in pursuit of the next clue, so they need to fly from north to south to get the best shots of the coast and avoid filling the lens with an expanse of empty sea. They also have to work out whether to film at high or low tide, depending on whether a clue is to

somewhere near the centre of each course as the communications van is based there during filming. There must be good sporting facilities, preferably a private dining-room, and various other features. Anne and Jenny do take some weekends off during their two-month tour, to do their washing and sample what have by then become culinary luxuries, such as baked beans on toast, in contrast to constant hotel food.

When they have achieved the almost impossible and have worked out the fifteen courses, these are presented to the producers and director, who go through them, help to iron out problems, add whatever extra ideas they have, and between them

be lodged on the beach or not. Sometimes alternative routes (and alternative clues) have to be allowed for in case the weather is bad and makes some part of the course unsafe or difficult to follow, or if some event – like using a lifeboat, perhaps, which might have to do some unscheduled rescue work – cannot take place.

This first 'recce' also gives Anne and Jenny a chance to sample the hotels that have been chosen to accommodate the whole team during filming in the summer. The hotels need to be situated

all choose the final locations. It is then up to Jenny to contact all the people she has met during the 'recce' to confirm with them that their property will be included, and to obtain permission for each element in each shoot to go ahead. As *Treasure Hunt* has become more widely known, so it has become easier to achieve this. Almost everybody is keen to help and happy to be included. Stately homes are particularly glad to be selected, as the number of visitors tends to rise dramatically during the summer after they are featured.

Before going on the first 'recce' Jenny will have given Keith Thompson, the *Treasure Hunt* skyrunner helicopter pilot, a general idea of where they are going; he will have responded by pointing out whether anything at that stage seems impossible. After the locations have been selected, the chosen landing sites for each clue are sent to Keith with the Ordnance Survey grid reference numbers. It is up to him to write to local airfields, to get landing and flight permissions from local air-traffic controllers, and to satisfy himself that the sites are safe. Safety is always at the front of his mind; however exciting the programme might become, it is never worth risking an accident. Malcolm and Keith have evolved a happy way of solving their disputes over precisely what constitutes a safe landing. While Malcolm is as aware as Keith of the importance of safety, their approaches are rather different: Keith sees it as a pilot, while Malcolm sees it as a producer who is constantly thinking about the scope of the programme. There are three 'jokers' per series, landing sites that are not actually dangerous, but that Keith is not entirely happy about. So Malcolm gets his way against Keith's reservations on three occasions . . . or, on one famous occasion – landing on a Royal Navy submarine out at sea – which needed such great skill on Keith's part that it used up all three 'jokers'. In fact, as Keith himself points out, that landing just required skill, but was not really all that dangerous. Trying to land in built-up areas is potentially far more dangerous than positioning yourself precisely on the narrow hull of a submarine. Anyway, as Malcolm is quick to point out, there's the whole ocean to land in if

you get it wrong, quite apart from the fact that the team all wore life jackets and frogmen were stationed near the sub in case anyone fell in!

At the same time as all the practical preparations for the programme get under way, negotiations begin between Chatsworth Television and Channel Four. Mike Bolland, the commissioning editor at Channel Four, tells Malcolm in November that a new series of *Treasure Hunt* is under consideration. Malcolm is asked to produce a detailed budget for making the series, and then discusses it with Channel Four's

production cost controller. The needs of *Treasure Hunt* have to be tailored to the funds available to Channel Four; there may be some hard bargaining before everyone is satisfied that the amount of money allocated will enable Malcolm to maintain the quality of the programmes. When the budget has finally been agreed, it goes to the finance committee for approval. It is then submitted to the main board of Channel Four for final approval. Only then can an offer letter be sent to Chatsworth; upon their acceptance of the offer, a contract is drawn up, the details negotiated, and

◄ Keith Thompson, Chief Pilot of Castle Air, whose skills contribute a great deal to the excitement of the programme.

▲ To Anneka waiting on the ground, and to the tense contestants in the studio, it seemed to take the Red Devils a long time to land, with great precision, one by one, at Capesthorne Hall in Cheshire, and she still had to find out which of them carried the clue.

the dotted line signed on.

This whole process takes several months to complete, so trust and understanding between Malcolm and Mike Bolland are essential. Finance is made available so that the research and planning can go ahead on the assumption that negotiations will be satisfactorily concluded in due course.

The producer of *Treasure Hunt* has all the usual tasks of a producer, and a few more. Malcolm likens the role of producer to that of the managing director of a company: he carries the can. It is up to the producer to organise the production of the series: he controls the staffing, the finances, makes sure that everything happens – and is responsible to the broadcaster for delivering what he said he would deliver, both in practical terms (i.e. the right number of programmes of the right length) and in terms of their quality. The producer of *Treasure Hunt* also doubles as location director, and is therefore closely involved with the programme creatively – a role that Malcolm, with many years of film-making experience behind him, enjoys.

With much of the detailed administration in hand, the month of May sees the second 'recce' take place. Keith flies a helicopter-load of the *Treasure Hunt* team to each location, and each course is carefully tested. Malcolm, Chris, Anne, Jenny and Keith himself are able to get a good idea of what the location will look like through Graham's lens, whether the sites are interesting and varied, whether there are any unforeseen problems that make a particular site undesirable. It is hard work: they take ten days to survey the courses for twelve programmes; with five clues and a start position to 'recce', and a hotel landing site, there is a total of over eighty landing sites to locate, as well as ensuring that the course chosen will be a good and exciting one.

The administrative process now starts all over again, as dates and sites are confirmed with the police, the Civil Aviation Authority, the local air-traffic controllers, local stately-home owners, landowners, councils, and everybody else on or over whose territory the shoot is to take place. It is part of Jenny's job to make the filming schedules work: to organise the itinerary so that they are filming at the right place on the right day, taking into account important local events, times of tides, and the availability of special events and personalities they wish to include. She also has to allow for breaks, as the location team always has Sundays off, and it is important to try to be somewhere congenial on that day where everyone

▲ There's no point in being a producer if you can't occasionally look like one! The rest of the team are happy to help Malcolm fulfil his fantasies during a break in filming.

▶ A busy day on the river Thames. The Radley Eight, with a larger-than-usual crew member in the person of Malcolm, watched by a passing pleasure launch and captured on film during rehearsal, with *below*, Anneka proving once again that girls can do just as well as the chaps, given the chance.

can relax – which usually means indulging in some strenuous sporting activity such as sailing, swimming or rounders. The locations are deliberately dotted around all over Britain, and producing an itinerary that works, allowing for travelling time, a rehearsal day and a filming day at each location, can be a nightmare.

Anne Evans can now start to write the clues. Her experience editing crosswords for the *Daily Telegraph* stands her in good stead, and she also has an enviable magpie mind for snippets of local information, as well as prodigious general knowledge. She admits modestly that most of the clues are compiled from within her own mind, but she checks that each part of each clue can be found in one of the reference books available to contestants. She also tries to get some general knowledge into each clue, so that viewers not familiar with an area and without specialist local reference works will nevertheless be able to solve at least part of it. If a site has historical or cultural interest, it makes the clue writing easier, something else that is borne in mind while the programmes are being planned.

Anne Evans tries to produce clues that can be solved in three stages. The first stage gets Anneka up in the air and heading in the right general direction; during the two or three minutes that it takes her to arrive, the second part of the clue will be puzzled out so that contestants can give her

precise instructions on where to land and what to do thereafter. The third part tells her what to look for.

Although the clues are written in relative peace and without undue pressure after the helicopter 'recce', Anne Evans' task is far from over. During filming she is part of the studio team, and may be called upon to change a clue or even to create a new one at the last moment. On one show she had a scant ten minutes in which to write a completely

▲ Months of training went into persuading Penny, the chimp, to yield up the clue card in return for a grape, but nobody had trained the Skyrunner, who cheerfully gave Penny an entire bunch of grapes before the card had been handed over – and then found the chimp refusing to keep to her side of the bargain.

▶ Watched by hundreds of spectators, the helicopter takes off against the magnificent background of Blenheim Palace in Oxfordshire.

▼ As usual surrounded by children, Anneka watches with real interest a demonstration of traditional weaving techniques at a folk museum in Wales.

new clue, as the famous cricketer, on whose presence at the first location the clue depended, had failed to turn up. Everything else was ready to go; and just in time the clue was ready too, hastily typed in the studio and telephoned through to Jenny in the outside broadcast van on location. On another occasion Anne Evans had to find a new location at the eleventh hour. In an effort to ensure that there would be plenty of people around while the programme was being made, a helpful stately home in Surrey advertised in the local paper that *Treasure Hunt* would be filming on a particular day. Malcolm got to hear of this, and of course the site had to be changed just in case the contestants or Anneka had learned about it. Because all the rest of the course for that programme had already been finalised, Anne

Evans had to find an acceptable alternative within a few miles of the first site, set up the visit and write the clue – all in the middle of the shooting schedule. On only one occasion did a change have to be made because the contestants had cleverly recognised the vaguest of outlines behind the covering over Wincey's map in the studio, correctly guessing Lake Windermere. As luck would have it, that was the one shoot in the series that was delayed because of bad weather, so the contestants were switched to a different day and different location without too much difficulty – and a new and thicker covering was put over Wincey's map.

Chris Gage, the director, and the production assistant, June Mason, also have a part to play in the preparation of the programme, though a good deal of their work takes place between filming and

▲ **Anneka on the balcony of one of Ludlow's famous Tudor landmarks, the Feathers Hotel.**

the time that the programmes are screened. In the early stages, Chris participates in the selection process for locations, joins Malcolm and the others on the helicopter 'recce', and liaises with the Ordnance Survey in Southampton for the right sheet maps to be ordered so that sections can be blown up into the large-scale artwork maps used in the studio. At a later stage she is involved in preparing the camera scripts for the studio cameras; only the first show of the series has a true camera rehearsal – after that there is just a quick camera rehearsal for Kenneth's introduction to the programme.

Chris began her career as a production secretary with the BBC, eventually progressing to vision mixing (the vision mixer is responsible for punching up the camera shots selected by the director) and then direction. She left the BBC to gain wider experience, and has survived two *Treasure Hunt* seasons. The 1986 filming is her third series; for her, the programme is particularly appealing because it is the only programme in which the studio and location pictures are joined up after shooting has been completed: working with studio pictures and only sound from location presents particular challenges. She also enjoys the immediacy and tension of working under live conditions.

During filming, Chris is in command of the

studio end from her control room, but her hardest period of work begins when for many of the team the year's work has almost finished. It takes five months of painstaking and careful work for Chris and Roy, the editor, to do the 'offline editing': creating a harmonious marriage between the location videotape and the studio tape, adding visual displays of clocks and clues to the master tape, editing and adding in the sound. The film editing process is still in progress when the researchers start their work planning the next year's series, so the baker's dozen *Treasure Hunt* programmes really do occupy the whole year.

The editing process has got easier with experience. Chris recounts that during her first year with the programme Malcolm went through her 'rough cut', the first edit, with a fine-toothed comb, and insisted on a considerable number of changes. But in subsequent years he has agreed almost entirely with what Chris has done. She has acquired an instinct for when to cut to location, when to keep the picture in the studio. There is a pattern to this: at the beginning of each clue there are quite a lot of studio shots, with contestants unravelling the clues. As the minutes tick away and Anneka gets nearer to each clue location the pictures tend to concentrate on her and the location, particularly as she redoubles her efforts to reach the vital treasure.

Because Chris particularly enjoys the hair-raising possibilities and split-second decision-making of live television, *Treasure Hunt*'s participation in the Thames Television Telethon for Children's Charities was specially exciting. For live shows the director has to edit instantly, in this case, all five studio cameras and the location shots, which were relayed to an extra monitor in the studio. It was some kind of miracle that the show worked at all, as the communications problems were formidable – indeed it wasn't until the evening before the Telethon took place that Nigel and Frank thought they had a chance of making it work at all.

Part of Chris's job is to shape the show. The overall programme has to occupy 51 minutes and 15 seconds of air time, excluding the commercial breaks. With the contest timed to last 45 minutes, she has just over 6 minutes for opening and closing the show, coming in to and out of breaks, and running the credits. This kind of precise timing becomes second nature to directors, but it has to be very carefully calculated, and at the same time Chris likes to include some variety – for example in Kenneth Kendall's introduction and preliminary chat with contestants – so the show does not begin to feel stale by the end of the series.

June Mason, production assistant, describes her part in *Treasure Hunt* as being responsible for ensuring that everything runs smoothly – which on a show that is constantly unpredictable represents a considerable challenge. During the preparatory stages she is involved with Anne and Jenny, typing up the clues, and also looking after copyright clearances and permissions. During the shoot she liaises with Jenny on location and Anne Evans and Chris Gage in the studio, and between them they somehow dodge the calamities – like the day that a boatyard at Hampton Court changed its mind about granting permission to land the day before shooting – luckily, the lock-keeper at Teddington Lock agreed to the helicopter landing there instead.

▼ **In the editing suite director Chris Gage (centre) studies the monitor screens, flanked by June Mason poised over the stopwatch and the programme editor, Roy Wolfe.**

'Lovely "comms", Nigel... Nigel?'

The key to *Treasure Hunt*'s success lies as much in its communications systems as in having good locations, satisfying clues and lively contestants. If Anneka and the contestants cannot hear each other clearly, the whole show grinds to a halt. Making sure that the 'comms' or communications are good is the job of Nigel Penton Tilbury, a freelance consultant engineer who spends half his time designing computer material and the other half acting as technical adviser to television programmes. He explained that firstly it is necessary for Anneka and the contestants in the studio to be able to communicate in a 'conversational environment' – that is, to have bi-directional radio links so they can both talk and listen at the same time, rather than saying 'Over' and flicking a switch as in conventional two-way radio. The speed of the programme, and the fact that the participants are doing several things at once and cannot concentrate only on smooth talking, makes this essential.

The signals from the microphones worn by the contestants in the studio travel via the mixer at Limehouse Studios down a special telephone line to the outside broadcast (OB) van on location. The lines are known in the jargon of the business as 'music lines', and are high-quality cables providing improved sound quality compared with standard telephone lines. They are rented from British Telecom, whose engineers install lines to the OB van at each location. The equipment in the OB van sends the signals out to the communications helicopter, from where they are beamed down to Anneka via her runner pack transceiver (transmitter/receiver). Similarly, what Annie herself says travels on a different frequency from her runner pack up to the 'comms' helicopter, down to the OB van, along the special phone lines to Limehouse, and through to the contestants' earpieces.

At the same time, what Anneka says is being recorded by the video recordist, Frank Meyburgh,

and can also be heard by Keith Thompson, pilot of the skyrunner helicopter, through his aircraft intercom systems, and cameraman Graham Berry through his earpieces, so he can where possible interpret what she is saying visually. The 'comms' helicopter has to be carefully positioned so that the best possible communications are maintained; sometimes it is necessary to 'bounce' the signals over obstructions, and the stationary OB van may be up to forty miles from the skyrunner's antics during the hunt. The van itself carries a 30-foot omni-directional aerial, with an additional 60-foot steerable beam antennae in reserve for locations where communications might prove particularly difficult to maintain – for example, in mountainous regions.

Nigel appreciates that for the pilots to understand what is happening, and to feel that they are a true part of the team, they too need to know what is going on. This is easy for Keith, but more difficult for Michael Malric-Smith, who is usually stationed several thousand feet above the ground away from all the action. Nigel produced a kit to monitor the quality of sound being obtained: apart from hearing both sides of the conversation through the intercom system, Michael looks at the signal strength meters to check whether his position is effective or not. The 'comms' helicopter has one aerial directed towards Anneka and another directed towards the base, so if the meters indicate that the signals are weak the pilot can reorientate the helicopter to improve the sound. Another refinement that Nigel introduced is the microphones. Ordinary pilots' mikes were used at first, but because the sound needs to be as free as possible of extraneous noise Nigel searched for an improved type, which has attracted a lot of attention from other professionals.

It is not only positioning the helicopter, and of course hoping that Anneka is not sent in search of a clue far inside a building with thick walls and no windows (castles can give particular problems)

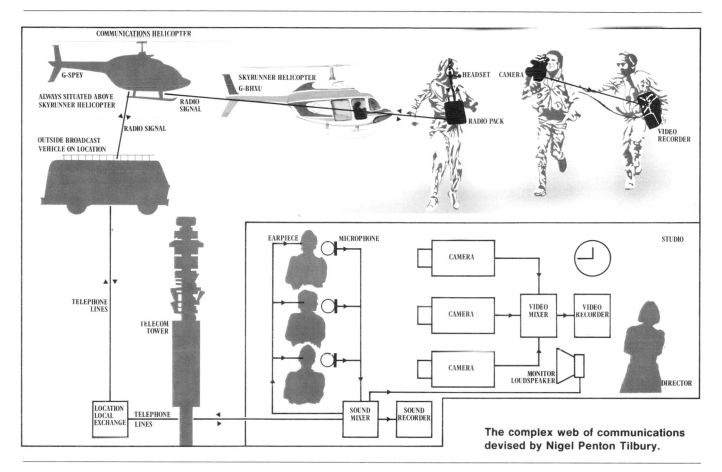

COMMUNICATIONS HELICOPTER

G-SPEY

ALWAYS SITUATED ABOVE
SKYRUNNER HELICOPTER

RADIO SIGNAL

SKYRUNNER HELICOPTER
G-BHXU

RADIO SIGNAL

HEADSET CAMERA

OUTSIDE BROADCAST
VEHICLE ON LOCATION

RADIO PACK

VIDEO
RECORDER

TELEPHONE
LINES

TELECOM
TOWER

EARPIECE   MICROPHONE

STUDIO

CAMERA

CAMERA

VIDEO
MIXER

VIDEO
RECORDER

CAMERA

MONITOR
LOUDSPEAKER

DIRECTOR

LOCATION
LOCAL
EXCHANGE

TELEPHONE
LINES

SOUND
MIXER

SOUND
RECORDER

**The complex web of communications
devised by Nigel Penton Tilbury.**

where signals cannot escape, that present Nigel's challenges. Changes in the weather and other environmental factors can affect the quality of communications too. For example, the team once flew over a glue factory where the radio-driven dryers (radio-driven dryers?) were co-incident with the radio frequencies Nigel was using, and interferred badly with programme communications. Those who know about radio will already be aware that the answer to this problem is to switch to a spare frequency that you happen to have about your person. Poor weather conditions can present hazards, too, but on the whole Nigel manages to keep to his instructions from Malcolm to produce good filming weather throughout the filming period. Occasionally, it almost proves too much even for Nigel's powers: in Florida, not only were the team unable to land at a chosen spot because it just happened to be under six feet of water after a hurricane, but the radios started to get the tell-tale sizzling sound they make just before a lightning flash; Nigel gritted his teeth until filming finished, and then gave permission for the weather to do what it had planned: the skies opened, and that was that for the rest of the day.

It is also Nigel's task to organise the renting of

the special telephone lines with British Telecom and, as every home telephone owner knows, this can be a time-consuming occupation. He is also responsible for liaising with the IBA, who contact local television companies to obtain permission for local broadcast frequencies to be used; Chatsworth is the only private television company to be granted permission to use TV station frequencies in each of the areas where shooting takes place. All the equipment needed to maintain good communications is duplicated, and they carry a good number of spares that might come in handy as well. Nigel is constantly experimenting with new equipment, and enjoys being able to test his new gadgets as soon as they are devised. His assistant, Philip Nowland, in the OB van is an expert in 'propagation': in getting signals transmitted, coping with atmospherics, siting aerials, and so on. Nigel himself makes sure that the sound is as clear as possible, monitors what is going wrong and thinks up rapid solutions to deal with the unexpected.

Not all the leading lights of *Treasure Hunt* are human. For some viewers, particularly aviation enthusiasts and small boys (or are they one and the same, of whatever age?), it is the helicopters that offer the big thrill of the show. The two

Augusta Bell 206B JetRanger helicopters used on the show belong to Castle Air Charters Ltd, a Cornwall-based company that specialises in film work as well as commercial and pleasure charter hire. The skyrunner's helicopter is piloted by Castle Air's Chief Pilot, Captain Keith Thompson, whose sense of humour and dedication to the programme alone qualify him for inclusion in the team, quite apart from his expertise in manoeuvring his craft into and out of some very tight corners. Captain Michael Malric-Smith's task is as difficult as Keith's; as pilot of the 'comms' helicopter, his role is vital in ensuring that radio links between the studio and Anneka are maintained throughout the course – regardless of weather conditions, the terrain over which they are flying, or whether Annie has disappeared into a dungeon. The dark green 'comms' helicopter has specially devised radio equipment in the rear cabin: two receivers and two transmitters, which are connected to three external aerials (one under the nose, one under the tail, and the third on the port skid strut). Michael's job is not only to maintain good communications, but also to keep in constant touch with local Air Traffic Control about what the two craft are doing, whether they are on schedule and what their intended movements will

be. If you are flying over Manchester International Airport you cannot just turn up a couple of minutes late and hope that you won't bump into anything. Keith Thompson relies on Michael to tell him if there are any problems with air-traffic control clearances regarding take-off or landing permissions, as during filming Keith makes no radio calls himself, though he can hear Anneka and Graham, and can also talk to Graham. Michael, on the other hand, needs to keep in constant communication with ATC (Air Traffic Control), and is simultaneously listening to several other people: his 'comms' assistant in the helicopter, the outside broadcast (OB) unit, Anneka, and sound from the studio. He is also constantly monitoring the strength of signals being transmitted to and from Anneka, thanks to the two special meters mounted at the top of his instrument panel. Add all that to having to fly a helicopter.

For Keith the great challenge of *Treasure Hunt* is flying and filming under time pressure. Most airborne film work does not have the stopwatch element – indeed, it is usually felt that getting good shots from a helicopter while flying at speed cannot be risked with just one 'take'. But on *Treasure Hunt* they do it. Keith's helicopter flies

with its tank only half full, which greatly improves manoeuvrability, and there is close contact between Keith and Graham while the latter is filming; with so much experience, Keith knows what Graham needs from him if the high standard of camerawork is to be maintained.

The Civil Aviation Authority has laid down rules about where and how aircraft may land. Keith has the ultimate veto over any landing sites suggested by the production team, though he and Malcolm sometimes have heated discussions about what is possible and what is not. Also, if weather conditions are poor, it may be Keith who declares that a programme has to be aborted. In one programme – on a misty day – they had begun the shoot with some trepidation and fingers crossed. Half-way through, Keith had achieved a tricky landing in an enclosed car park next to a factory. While Anneka was inside the building, dense fog suddenly descended, and Keith refused to budge. The shoot had to be abandoned, and the clock was stopped. They came back some days later, on a sunny day, to carry on where they had left off. Anneka came running out of the building, looked up at the sky and declared with perfect aplomb: 'My goodness, it has cleared up a bit while we've been in there.'

◄ ◄ **(From left) Frank Meyburgh, Nigel Penton Tilbury, Graham Berry, Philip Nowland, Keith Thompson, Anneka Rice, Michael Malric-Smith, Peter Jones, Malcolm Heyworth, Angela Breheny, Dennis Squibb, Jenny Gradwell.**

▲ **Inside the 'comms' helicopter, Michael Malric-Smith has to keep an eye on both the studio and Skyrunner signals meters as well as flying and maintaining links with local ATC.**

▼ **A fuel tanker comes on location.**

During the programme's prepatory stages, Keith will study maps, brief airfields and discuss routes and timings with local air-traffic controllers. Not only do the civil airfields need to be kept informed, but military bases as well – sometimes with unexpected results. While filming in West Yorkshire, after having gone through all the usual formalities, Keith and his passengers almost leaped out of their skins when an RAF Jaguar screamed past the nose of the helicopter. Michael contacted the local ATC, who said that they were sorry but military activities were kept secret and they didn't know anything about what might be going on. This flight had an unusual excitement, as Jaguars and Tornados continued to speed above, below, in front of and behind the poor helicopter and its bewildered pilot. Keith decided that they were being used as target practice by the local RAF training school!

By the time the series is to be filmed, Keith will have a fair idea of their routes and landing sites, Keith having done the helicopter 'recce' in May as well as the rehearsal run the day before shooting the actual programme. But he cannot afford to be complacent; there is still the question of whether the contestants will solve the clue correctly and send him off where he is expecting to go, or invent a wild goose chase for him and ask him to make an unscheduled landing. Keith will fly where he is asked to fly, and on occasion has landed somewhere totally unexpected. The only time a contestant's instruction was completely countermanded was when Keith was asked to fly to Inverness when the city was not even on the studio map. On this occasion Kenneth Kendall did tactfully suggest that perhaps a different solution to the clue was needed; the contestant who had made the request was hard to convince.

▼ **Frank, Graham, Anneka and Keith relax during a break in filming.**

Life behind the lens

In spite of his somewhat unbecoming skullcap, for many viewers Graham Berry is the hero of *Treasure Hunt*. He says that the beginning of the shooting season each year is like a big family reunion – a view echoed by all the other members of the team. They all look forward to the intense, exhausting five weeks they spend together, enclosed in a world of their own, cosseted by Malcolm and his insistence that they need to stay in pleasant hotels, eat first-rate meals and generally be spoilt to offset the gruelling effects of their filming schedule.

One of Graham's reasons for enjoying the work so much is the freedom it gives him to work his own way. He and Malcolm will discuss in general terms what is required, and the rehearsal day gives them both some idea of particular items to film and how to do it. The rehearsal also gives Graham a chance to encounter relatively at leisure any new obstacles or hazards that the researchers have dreamed up: running across stepping stones without getting the camera as well as his feet wet, jumping in and out of boats, diving into cavernous tunnels, and so forth. But on the shoot itself, with Anneka running over the course for the first time, and with an unrehearsed group of extras in members of the public who may suddenly be asked to participate, Graham has plenty of scope for interpreting shots in his own way, filming something that might be quirky or amusing or surprising. And that challenge, that responsibility, is not often found – there's usually a director at the cameraman's elbow telling him exactly what shots to go for. The extra independence is a great stimulus, and Graham is constantly looking for ways to improve his work. It is hardly surprising that he won the 1984 Video Cameraman of the Year award for his work on *Treasure Hunt*.

Video cameras have their limitations: they cannot cope with excessive contrast in light and shade, nor with hot skies. Graham's Ikegami 79D camera has a 'zebra' fitted into it which gives him

▲ ▲ One of the programme's most spectacular feats was to land on a Royal Navy submarine out at sea.

▲ Not all the clues are on little pink cards. This one had to be read from the airborne helicopter in hot pursuit of a power boat, which needed some careful planning to get the timing right.

an indication of the camera's highlight handling capacity at any given moment. With so much experience of handling a shoulder-held camera while running full tilt after Anneka's much loved – but often rapidly disappearing – rear view, Graham now operates the camera largely on auto-pilot. 'While I'm running,' he explained, 'I no longer have my eye to the camera very much, it sort of looks after itself.' He needs to keep an eye on Annie's antics, to see good new shots in what she is doing, and often to try to film the clue before Annie finds it, so the audience knows where it is before she does. Of course if the clue has disappeared, his job is less easy. On one occasion the treasure, a little gold horse hidden under a white stone that is the eye of the White Horse on the Berkshire Downs, had disappeared between rehearsal and filming. Graham realised what had happened, changed his filming sequence at the last moment, and later the discovery of a replacement treasure (in fact a screwed-up piece of gold paper from a cigarette packet) was filmed from the air and edited in so that nobody was any the wiser. On another occasion the clue was eaten by lion cubs.

Graham has to be very fit to be able to cope with all the running about he is expected to do, particularly as he has 23 lb of camera added to his own weight. In order to hold the camera still enough to get a constantly steady picture, he has developed a very individual running style, a sort of lope moving from the waist down and holding the upper part of his body as still as possible. Put a big cigar between his lips and change the hair colour, and he would be almost indistinguishable from a

◀ Graham's job would not suit those who don't have a head for heights – and he has to trust Frank, who connects his safety straps for him.

▲ The most popular method of transport in Oxford is the bicycle – but if you're a video recordist with a broken basket you've got problems. Ever resourceful, Frank holds the vital cable in his teeth, steers the bike with one hand and holds the basket with the other as he pedals after Annie and Graham along Broad Street.

certain Groucho Marx. He trains (without camera to shoulder) for about three months before the team goes out on location, having discovered during the auditions what happens to an unfit cameraman who has to run after athletes.

The orange suits worn by Graham and Frank during filming were Graham's own choice. They were originally designed to be worn by German pilots, and were intended to attract search and rescue teams looking for pilots in the sea. But, according to Graham, their bright colour attracted sharks, who tended to get there first, so they were withdrawn. The name of Graham's company, the Flying Camera Co., was embroidered on the front by Graham himself.

Another of Graham's talents is as a mimic. He has a wonderful repertoire: Prince Charles, Ronald Reagan, Robin Day, and the sound of JetRanger helicopter engines being started up, which almost gave pilot Keith Thompson cardiac arrest as he

blithely unaware of the fact that he had nearly done an unscheduled backwards somersault. The thing about *Treasure Hunt* is that you cannot get back to the surface and say to Malcolm, 'Sorry Malc, we had a spot of bother and lost that sequence, so we'll need to shoot it all over again.' You have to think quickly enough to get out of trouble before you're really in it.

Frank's professional background no doubt helps him to act quickly in a crisis. In the past he spent three months with the British monitoring force in

sipped a well-earned drink one evening in a hotel in the Lake District – confident until that moment that his precious flying machine was resting safely on the lawns outside.

Life would be easier for Frank Meyburgh if someone would put on his or her thinking cap and invent a camera/recorder system small and compact enough for one person to use for *Treasure Hunt*. There is something specially enjoyable, though, in the sight of Graham and Frank running in tandem, connected by the umbilical cord linking the camera with the video recorder under Frank's arm. It is up to Frank to ensure that the video cable does not trip anyone up, or become entangled round gateposts or other natural hazards: the closest to disaster they have come was shooting a sequence down a Welsh mine, following Anneka on a little cart that runs through the tunnels. The cable got caught up round a guide light in the tunnel, and Frank managed to free it only just in time as they shot past, with Graham

Rhodesia (Zimbabwe nowadays), and during the 1970s he spent several years doing sound and editing in war zones such as Angola, Namibia and Mozambique. He is a man who likes a challenge, and after some hair-raising war experiences was glad to have a challenge of a different kind when Malcolm approached Crystal Films to see whether his ideas on how *Treasure Hunt* should be filmed could be managed technically. One big difference between war reporting and making feature programmes is that the IBA (Independent Broadcasting Authority) gives dispensation to news and current affairs items, which do not have to conform to the strict technical standards laid down in the IBA Specification. To keep the *Treasure Hunt* equipment up to standard and to make sure that what is produced is always of broadcast quality, Frank spends several hours each day on location checking, tinkering, adjusting the Ikegami cameras, which combine lightness and stability with various technical advantages such as very reliable registration (the matching of colour from the three tubes). One technical problem that cannot always be overcome by talented engineering precision is with the servo, the major transport mechanism for the tape carried in Frank's video recorder. Recording difficulties arise if the tape is unstable, and the tape is unstable if the poor engineer running with it is not fit enough, and is getting tired and running unevenly or puffing too much. This did happen in the first series, since when Frank too goes into serious

thousand feet up. Frank might not entirely agree.

Frank's video recorder is a Sony BVU (broadcast video unit). It is up to him to ensure that everything Annie says is recorded, and also that when she is talking to people their conversation (picked up by the extra microphone attached to the front of her suit) is included on tape. For Annie's voice he has more than one sound source to choose from, and has to remain on the alert, checking which source offers the clearest sound, while he jumps in and out of the helicopter, remembers to

training some three months before shooting starts each year, running several miles every day in spite of other commitments to make sure that he will be able to keep up comfortably with the others.

Filming in war zones gave Frank some good first-hand experience with helicopters. 'I have a love–hate relationship with them still,' he says. 'When I'm in one I feel really scared, but when I'm on the ground I just long to get back in for another ride.' You will never know that all this conflict is going on, as Frank deftly unhooks Graham's anchor straps and follows him nimbly out of the helicopter to chase after Anneka in pursuit of another clue.

Graham does not have the same problem. He maintains that you don't get vertigo if you are already out of contact with the ground. He assured me that it was much more scary leaning out at an angle on a mountainside, filming someone rock-climbing, than it is to lean out of a helicopter to film some choice bit of scenery from several

▲ **The beach at Brighton has never seemed longer . . . our intrepid heroine, with two heroes in her wake, manages to keep running for some three-quarters of a mile, laughing and filming all the way.**

fasten and release Graham's anchor straps as well as his own, looks after the video cable, makes sure he is out of camera shot, guides Graham past hazards . . . no wonder he sometimes looks a trifle harassed.

◀ **This pig at Acton Scott Farm Museum, Shropshire, listened intently to Anneka's greeting.**

... and in front of the lens

To most of us, the idea of appearing on television, particularly in a situation where we might make fools of ourselves, is terrifying. But not to everyone. The numbers of people applying to be considered as contestants on *Treasure Hunt* has grown each year, and in 1986 reached a staggering 6,000 couples. Pity poor Angela Breheny, whose job it is to read through 12,000 application forms and try to decide who would made good contestants. It takes a month just to assess the applications. Having whittled the numbers down to some 250 couples, Angela and Victoria Bartleet are off on their travels round the country (to Bristol, Liverpool, Birmingham, Leeds and Southampton, as well as London) to interview those who have survived the first stage of the selection process. Of those interviewed, twenty pairs are asked to a second interview, at which the producers are present. Then a final selection of the lucky thirteen pairs is made.

It is difficult to identify exactly what makes a good contestant. They obviously have to be articulate, to know how to read a map and how to use reference books. But it is their personality that is more important. 'We are looking for bright, intelligent, witty, attractive people,' Angela explains. 'Actually it is more important for contestants to be talkative and entertaining than

▼ Kenneth Kendall and a pair of nervous contestants await the beginning of a show with a floor manager.

that they should be terribly good at solving the clues. That's preferable to their being clever but dull – which makes dreadful television.' They are constantly on the lookout for a wider variety of contestants, trying to avoid a preponderance of middle-aged teachers and librarians from the Home Counties. It is not always easy, but in a random look through the application forms there is a good range of occupations: policeman, electrical engineer, solicitor's clerk, priest, accounts clerk, auxiliary nurse, farmer, chartered accountant, design draughtsman, teacher, micropalaeontologist (he'd have had to be brainy just to spell his profession!), copy reader on the *Financial Times*, hairdresser, jazz pianist, roulette and blackjack inspector in a West End casino, Open University professor, postman.

The interviews themselves are enlightening. Because so much of the success of the show depends on the personalities of the contestants, they need to make a good and reasonably extrovert impression at their interview. Some candidates do, and the interview runs over time as everybody chats away about *Treasure Hunt* and what they think of it, questions are asked about the way the programme is made, the contestants explain why they want to go on the show, and so forth. Others seem very shy and withdrawn, and answer briefly questions put to them without responding very much. During the interview, candidates are asked to tackle a sample clue: they stand in front of a map, with a few reference books to hand, while Angela and Victoria role-play Kenneth and Anneka. Some of the most confident interviewees visibly wilt when faced with this ordeal, while some of the quieter candidates suddenly perk up and begin to perform. High points are scored by candidates who read through their clue and remember to say to 'Annie', 'Please get into the helicopter and take off; just hover till we've worked out where you need to go.' All the contestants seem to find even this taste of what it is like in the hot seat quite nerve-wracking, and get to the end with pulse racing, heart thumping, and hands distinctly clammy. So what must it be like in the studio?

Most candidates seem to apply partly because they think it would be fun, and partly because, sitting at home each week often reaching the answers before the contestants themselves have solved the clues, they are tempted to prove that on screen they could also do better. One lady from Clwyd takes the game so seriously that she confessed she had never actually seen a

programme, though she had heard all of them. In order not to have an unfair advantage over the contestants in the studio, she turns her back when the clock is started, and only listens to what is going on while she tries to work out the answers!

The interview begins to show potential contestants that it is perhaps not so easy after all. Not having the visual aids that we see watching the show on television makes an enormous difference. If the clue mentions 'onion-tops' and you can see a stately home looming up with onion-shaped domes on its roof, you know you've got it right, but the contestants cannot see anything, and they have to puzzle it out for themselves while trying to remember to listen to Annie's descriptions and suggestions. She is their eyes as well as their feet, but with all the other distractions in the studio it is not always easy to attend to what she is saying.

Those who do make it through the selection process, and find themselves three months later speeding from their hotel to Limehouse Studios, may be in for a few surprises. Contestants are often amazed by how genuinely friendly all the studio team seem to be. Great efforts are made to explain everything that is going on, to make them feel welcome and to put them at their ease, and to assure them that everybody does actually want them to win. This can make a big difference to pre-filming nerves, and it is important because the one thing that the selection process cannot weed out is the contestant who seems fine, but then suffers such terrible stage fright that he or she cannot perform in front of the cameras at all. It has been known for large glasses of champagne to be given to contestants during the first commercial break in an effort to get them to relax.

The contestants are shown round the studio and given a chance to familiarise themselves with the library of books at their disposal. The books and pamphlets particularly relevant to 'their' show are not put out until a few minutes before filming begins. The day before the show they also undergo a full rehearsal – not with the location team, who are busy having their own rehearsal to run through the course for the next day, but they do have real clues for a real location taken from an earlier programme, against the clock, with Kenneth and Wincey in the studio and the director, Chris Gage, in Annie's role and out of sight. Even though they know it is not the real thing, the pressure does build up as the minutes tick away, and the contestants get a good idea of what it is going to be like on the day.

In recent series filming has begun at about 10.30 a.m. Contestants are told the evening before what time they will be collected from their hotel; if they are told to be ready at 3 p.m. or, worse, 3 a.m., they will guess that theirs is to be the one foreign location in the series, as filming tends to begin at about 10.30 a.m. local time wherever the location team happens to be. There seems to be a good deal of finger-crossing among contestants that they have not been paired up with the 'special'. It does add an extra dimension of difficulty to their task, particularly if, as has happened, the map appears and you discover that it covers a portion of Israel . . . and that most of the names are given in Hebrew!

Many contestants seem to be surprised by the secrecy surrounding the programme. They are never left alone in the studio; Kenneth is quite obviously as much in the dark as they are; members of the crew are immensely careful not to let slip anything that might be remotely useful in giving away a location. Even at the last minute, when they have a warm-up chat with Anneka shortly before filming starts, she (who knows nothing in detail, but by this time does actually know where she is) is likely to mislead rather than inform.

One pair of constestants was asked: 'Can you hear the waterfall in the background?' and then heard her say, 'Graham, what did you have for lunch?' She admitted afterwards that she had wanted them to think she was standing by Niagara Falls, whereas in fact she was by a fountain in Dyffryn Gardens near Cardiff. One of the contestants on that day, Olivia Deighton, says of the experience: 'I would do it again tomorrow if they'd have me. It was terrific.' Unusually, she didn't suffer badly from nerves before the programme was filmed; she was much more ill at ease the day it was to be broadcast, wondering how she would come across and what her friends would think. Olivia and her brother Charles had not even entered themselves as contestants: their father suggested to Chatsworth that they would make good contestants, and it went on from there. She was astounded by the friendliness of everyone in the studio. When they were discussing what location they hoped they might get, Charles said: 'Anywhere but Wales for me, as I can't pronounce the names,' so it was almost inevitable that Wales is where they would end up.

The Wales show provided a good example of how Anneka can really help the contestants, and also how she can slow down their progress. After negotiating the log flume (a cross between a boat ride and a big dipper) at a fun fair, Annie discovered from someone in the crowd that the clue she had just found referred obliquely to the folk museum at St Fagan's. When Annie eventually arrived there the constestants had worked out that she had to collect the clue from a sheep with a ribbon round its neck. It was one of a small flock, complete with shepherd and dog. In her enthusiasm Annie, rather than asking the shepherd to get his dog to round up the sheep, ran after them herself. It made great viewing, seeing Anneka haring after the sheep shouting 'Here boy!' as they scattered in all directions, but it was frustrating for the contestants, as the clock remorselessly showed the minutes ticking away.

Like the rest of the team, Anneka wants the contestants to win, and works as hard for them as she can. On this particular occasion they ran out of time just as Annie approached the 'treasure': the Welsh dragon flag that she had spotted from the air was almost within her grasp when the gong sounded. It had been a very close-run thing, and Annie sounded genuinely disappointed as she said goodbye. 'I'm so sorry we didn't get there, you were fantastic.' The studio team evidently thought so too, as the magnum of champagne normally reserved for contestants who solve the bonus clue was presented to Charles and Olivia in consolation. One of the ingredients for a good show is a nail-biting finish – and that they certainly did achieve.

▼ **Anneka at the start point talks to the studio and then describes the location.**

Ready to go...

Some time in June, at a peaceful hotel in some secret location in a lovely part of Britain, a convoy of vehicles will draw up: a Toyota Landcruiser, a Winnebago towing a fuel tanker, and a large van. Shortly afterwards the air will be filled with the sound of helicopter motors as one yellow-and-white and one dark metallic green helicopter drop out of the sky onto the hotel lawn. There will be joyous cries of greeting. *Treasure Hunt* has taken to the roads again. For the location team this is a happy time. When everyone has calmed down a bit, they will start to unload, everybody helping (skyrunner and producer included – there's no standing on ceremony or union demarcation in this show). The routine of the next few weeks has started again: arrive at a location, get organised, rehearsal day, filming day, then pack up and drive or fly to the next location, unload and get organised, rehearsal day, and so on.

The following morning it is time for rehearsal. Anneka is left behind at the hotel, deserted for the day by the entire crew. On rehearsal day she just tries to keep out of everyone's way; it is strange to have nothing particular to do while everyone else is so busy, though the hotels are chosen partly for their amenities, and Anneka is hardly the type to sit around twiddling her thumbs all day.

The others all go off to their allotted tasks. The action sheets prepared by Jenny are distributed to the team. They contain names of contestants, details about the hotel, other important contact numbers, such as the local police, the clues and where they lead to, details of sites, estimated times of arrival for rehearsal and recording days, landing positions, the exact positions of clue cards, names and phone numbers of the contacts at each site.

The rehearsal takes place over the exact course that Anneka will run the following day – if the contestants are getting the right answers to the clues. Malcolm dons the runner pack for the rehearsal. It gives Graham and Frank a chance to practise filming for the morrow; Nigel and the

'comms' helicopter establish that communications can be maintained and that any special problems – such as siting the helicopter precisely in line with a particular window so that the sound can be beamed clearly to and from Annie inside the building – can be solved. Malcolm checks that the course is safe – that there is no risk of Anneka or her two faithful followers getting hurt. This is also Malcolm's opportunity to meet all the officials and other contacts – from dukes to parachutists – whose help is needed on the day, to brief them about what he would like them to do, to hand over the precious clue cards and to finalise any other arrangements, such as persuading gardeners to act as crowd controllers.

During the rehearsal the timings are noted down literally to the second by Jenny: from start position to helicopter, flight times from one landing position to the next, and how long it takes Malcolm,

▼ The outside broadcast van and Toyota Landcruiser, just two of the vehicles needed to ferry the location team from place to place.

Graham and Frank to run from landing site to clue
position and back again. Experience has proved
that a course lasting $37\frac{1}{2}$ minutes when run without
any hesitation, deviation or repetition by someone
who knows where the clues are, is most likely to
give the kind of nail-biting finish that makes for a
good show in television terms, even if it is hard on
the nerves of the contestants. Once these timings
are known, Jenny telephones them through to June
on one of the special lines linking the OB van to
the studio. On the day the real timings are also
carefully noted, and checked against the previous
day's figures. June feeds through to Wincey details
of how the contestants are getting on, and the
timings are also used to decide where the
commercial breaks are taken. Sometimes, the
commercial breaks are used to reposition the
helicopter and/or the skyrunner to ensure that the
course runs for the prescribed length, and to start
again in a particularly attractive spot. The course
has been worked out to include this occasional
feature.

The rehearsal will take most of the morning; the
afternoon is spent going through the film made
and the sound recorded during the rehearsal.
Everybody assesses the morning's work from his
own point of view: Malcolm will be looking at the
overall quality of the programme, Jenny will study
timings, Graham and Frank will take a critical look
at light and sound levels all the way through, Nigel
will be checking for communications weaknesses.

During the evening everyone relaxes, and
Anneka is allowed to rejoin the rest of the team.
They are extraordinarily careful not to talk about
what they have been doing all day, difficult though
it is. Only now will Anneka be given her map for
the following day's location – and even this only
gives her a vague idea of the general area, nothing
specific – together with the 'FFs': fascinating facts
that Anne Evans has prepared for Anneka to
introduce the programme.

On the morning of the shoot there is tension in
the air before the time comes for everyone to get
going. The helicopters have been refuelled,
checked and polished. Annie is dressed in one of
the specially designed, eye-catching suits. With
Annie, Graham and Frank on board, the runner
helicopter moves off to the start position closely
followed by the 'comms' helicopter, which will
shadow it during the shoot. Malcolm, Nigel and
Jenny retire to the OB van. There is not much
room in the van, and they will spend the next
couple of hours trying not to get too much in each
other's way. They all need to monitor what is

happening, but they have only sound with which to do it. Jenny spends most of her time on the telephone, either talking to the studio on the direct link line, or using one of the two ordinary telephones to maintain contact with officials at each of the landing sites so they know when Annie's arrival is imminent.

When the helicopters arrive at the start position there is time for everyone to look around. Anneka's runner pack is checked and adjusted, she dons her headset, sound is established between her and the studio and she can start to chat to the contestants while Nigel begins to monitor sound quality. They are ready.

In the meantime, in the studio the tension has also been mounting. Cups of coffee have been drained, the contestants' earpieces have been fitted and are beginning to emit the strange squeaks and squeals that will soon settle down into the familiar sequence of helicopter motors and Annie's voice. The contestants are beginning to wish that they had never embarked on this extraordinary adventure – or perhaps are feeling calm and cool and just determined to do their best. The lights are on, the studio cameras are starting to run, Chris Gage is in her director's chair and her assistants are at the ready. Kenneth Kendall continues to smile encouragement at the victims, Wincey has the clues at the ready. She actually knows all about today's location, so it is hardly surprising that she looks relaxed and cheerful.

Suddenly the studio floor clears of all but the contestants, Kenneth and Wincey. Anneka's voice has been coming over loud and clear, but now falls silent. A voice says, 'Ready to go . . . and *cue!*' Kenneth smiles into the camera:

'*Hallo, and welcome to this week's Treasure Hunt*'.

◄ Anneka caused quite a stir in the crowded Tank Museum at Bovington (and Malcolm, in the top picture, had fun on rehearsal day). It isn't often that pretty, jumpsuit-clad girls can be found clambering around on the exhibits.

The Producers,
Treasure Hunt,
Channel Four.

Dear Sirs,
        I felt I had to write to tell you how much pleasure you give to me and my wife and quite a few office colleagues with Treasure Hunt; and also to give you a laugh at my expense.
        For an hour on Thursday evenings (this year and the past two) I have been the untouchable, not in to visitors, out to telephone callers; totally uncommunicative to the rest of the family unless they are able to buy my time by providing a map reference or throw new light on a cryptic clue.   I surround myself with every available map, tourist guide AA/Readers Digest tome which were foolishly bought and never used until Anneke took to the air.   And there is I sit, surrounded by encyclopaedias yelling at your studio guests, shrieking with glee when I beat them to a clue, looking sullen when I don't and at the end of it feeling daft at getting so exc   After all, it's only a programme and as a newspaper jou   hard-bitten cynic above all that sort of

        Anyway, pass on   al
and Graham and.... a

April 6th 1985

Dear sirs,

    I have to hasten to say that I have never been in the dubious either fan or abusive letters to the media. But I must express reciation for what has now become one of my favourite television called "Treasure Hunt". Since I have first watched it I have especially for the excellent Kenneth Kendal and that s. No one could do the job better, and they certainly

    I must conf   that the main reason for writing this ss Anneka Rice gives me, a truly e a genuine involvement and s in passing to me, an ageing behind him, her own sense of t my age, I have to be an avid art from sitting and gawking e I am able to offer my ell as the most enticing e Hunt Special last night

19/2/86

Dear Anneka Rice
    I am writing to you to let you know how much I enjoy watching you on the Treasure Hunt programme. You are so lively and always doing interesting things. I would be very pleased if you could send me a signed photograph of yourself.
            Thank you very much
            Zoe Stanson (age 7 years)

what the actual programme was videoed during 1984 and that "next year" THIS year, 1985. I really can't 1i

Armchair Treasure Hunt Competition

Kenneth Kendall's Pointers on how to solve the Treasure Hunts

The following ten Armchair Treasure Hunts are based on ten maps (published by courtesy of the Michelin Tyre company). On this page is the key to the various symbols on the maps.

KEY

Roads

Motorway with numbered junctions: complete - half - limited . . . .

Service areas . . . .

Dual carriageway with interchanges : complete - half - limited . . . . .

Official road classification :
Motorway - Primary route . . . .
Other roads . . . .

M 5   A 3 !
A 155   B 142

Direction sign for places on primary route network . . . .

YORK

Major road :
dual carriageway . . . .
4 lanes - 2 wide lanes . . . .
2 lanes - 2 narrow lanes . . . .
Regional road network :
dual carriageway - 2 wide lanes . . . . .
2 lanes - 2 narrow lanes . . . .
Other roads : surfaced - unsurfaced . . . . .

In Scotland : narrow road with passing places . . . .
Road under construction . . . .
Footpath - Long distance footpath or bridleway . . . .
Roundabout - Pass with altitude (in metres)   96

Gradient :
(ascent in the direction of the arrow) . . . .
1:7-1:5   +1:5
14-20%   +20%

Distances on motorways and roads :
in miles   14   10
in kilometres   24   39
Prohibited road - Road subject to restrictions . . . . . .
Road, bridge, tunnel with toll - One-way road . . . .
Scheduled opening date   12-85

Railways

Standard gauge - Passenger station . . . .
Steam railways - Industrial track . . . .
Industrial cable way - Chair lift . . . .
Level crossing, railway passing under road, over road . . . .

Car ferries :
Seasonal services : in red

boat . . . .
hovercraft . . . .

ferry (maximum load : in metric tons) . . . . . .

Foot passengers and bicycles only . . . . .

Towns - Administration

Towns having a plan in the Michelin Red Guide . . . .
Town included in the above Michelin Guide . . . .

Ambleside

County or regional boundary . . . .
Scottish and Welsh borders . . . .

Other symbols

Telecommunications aerial . . . .
Factory - Power station . . . .
Refinery - Mine - Lighthouse . . . .
Isolated hotel - Racecourse . . . .
Golf course (visitors welcome) . . . .
Caravan and camping sites . . . .
Racing circuit - Pleasure boat harbour . . . . .
National Forest Park, National Park . . . .
Forest walk . . . .
Country park - Cliff . . . .

Airport - Airfield . . . .

Principal sights :
see Michelin Red Guide

Ecclesiastical building - Ruins . . . .
Castle, historic house . . . .
Megalithic monument - Cave . . . .
Safari park zoo - Nature reserve, seabird colony . . . . .
Gardens, park - Miscellaneous sights . . . .

Panorama - Viewpoint . . . .

Towns or places of interest, places to stay . . . . .   **Rye** (▲)   **Elgol**

Scenic route . . . .

Each Treasure Hunt consists of ten clues. Each clue directs the reader to a place on the map, and the final answer to the clue might be the name of that place. More often, however, it is a name(s) or word(s) arising out of something or somebody connected to that place. The connection might be slight or fanciful or cryptic, but the information to solve the clue is always contained within it. To make these connections, a certain amount of general knowledge, plus a knowledge of the history, geography or customs of a place is required. It is unlikely that anybody will be able to answer all the clues without the occasional consultation of a reference book. The television contestants have a library to hand, of course, because they must work fast. The object here has been to limit the books required to those which might be stocked in a public library.

The following list is not meant to be exhaustive, but to illustrate the kind of book which will be found useful.

1 *Guides such as:*
The Ward Lock Red Guide Series
The Visitors Guide Series (Morland Publishing)
Holiday Which? Touring Guide Series
The Bartholomew Series of guides

The Companion Guide Series (Collins)
The Shell Guide Series (Faber and Faber)
The New Shell Guide to England (Michael Joseph)
The New Shell Guide to Britain (Ebury Press)
The Portrait Series (Robert Hale)

2 *General books such as:*
AA Treasures of Britain (Drive Publications)
Historic Houses of Britain by Mark Girouard (Peerage Books)

3 *Personal reminiscences and observations such as:*
A Walk around the Lakes by Hunter Davies (Weidenfeld and Nicolson, 1979)
Wiltshire by Ralph Whitlock (B.T. Batsford Ltd., 1976), and so on.

The Treasure Hunts are graded roughly in order of difficulty: easiest first.

Each Treasure Hunt includes a Treasure Chest, a box in which to write the answers to the clues. Where the answer contains more than one word do not leave spaces between words. Each filled Treasure Chest reveals a key word related to the map.

Readers who solve each Treasure Hunt can use the key words to enter the competition.

Good luck!

TREASURE HUNT Competition

WIN £1,000
See page 98 for Rules

TREASURE HUNT·1

Clue 1 Begin this Treasure Hunt, naturally, with the noble Goddess of Hunting, and the place invested with significance by her spouse. It's the first Treasure for the Chest.

Clue 2 Fly northeast to where three bridges lead to eight towers. Take the tube and find the rocketry expert who built it.

Clue 3 Southeastwards to where the Ladies lived and the hills are alive to the sound of foreign music. Pass up the road and find a lucky symbol.

Clue 4 Climb west now to the heights of Royal photography, before descending by rail to where rainbells are made. This place goes in the Chest.

Clue 5 Quick march to the men of this town. Besieged for eight years they later held a moving picture franchise. Put the town in the Chest.

Clue 6 Go east now to where the town centre is west and find nearby the man who turned to find a fortune, so appropriately can go into the Treasure Chest.

Clue 7 Northwest to a town with a Happy Valley and a memorial to Lewis Carroll. Unfortunately, with half a dozen Romans it can be rendered null and void. Put it in the Chest anyway.

Clue 8 Go southwest to an insular place where a Hans Andersen heroine offers drinks. She should go in a sea chest!

Clue 9 Southeastwards now to half a treble chance column, the Australian cricketers' Castlemaine, two pairs of kisses, three Maltese plus a double, or maybe wrong each time – anyway put them all in the Chest.

Clue 10 Fly northwest with the birds, to where a lighthouse shines on the land smokin and blowin in the sea. Give the Treasure Chest the bird.

CLUE 6 ▶

WITH ROYALS AND CASTLES ·IN WALES· AND THE· MARCHES

#										
1	C	A	E	R	N	A	R	E	O	N
2	S	T	E	P	H	E	N	S	O	N
3	H	O	R	S	E	S	H	O	E	
4	L	L	A	N	D	E	R	I	S	
5	H	A	R	L	E	C	H			
6	W	H	I	T	T	I	N	G	T	O	N
7	L	L	A	N	D	U	D	N	O	
8	M	E	R	M	A	I	D	I	N	N
9	F	O	U	R	C	R	O	S	S	E	S
10	P	U	F	F	I	N				

Treasure Chest key word:
The letters can be made into a popular range of giant's highchair (two words).

58

CADER IDRIS

CLUE 7 ▲

◄ CLUE 2

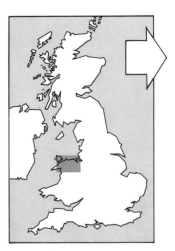

Armchair TREASURE HUNT-1

WITH ROYALS AND CASTLES IN WALES AND THE MARCHES

TREASURE HUNT-2

Clue 1 Start at the cattle crossing where the stair rail ran for a mile, and put into the Treasure Chest the museum which starts where a cigarette ends and contains a spy.

Clue 2 The foamy crest of a wave leads you southwest down its vale to the viewpoint from its hill – put into the Chest the ancient path which crests the hill.

Clue 3 Eastwards now where one of the social events of the year could lead to a right Royal row and heroes belong to Leander. Find the silver vessels for the unaccompanied couple.

Clue 4 To the northwest where John was given a pile and a dukedom for defeating the French and his descendant was born to defeat the Germans. Put their surname into the Chest.

Clue 5 Fly in an easterly direction to the home of the white duck, and the nearby manor house full of French treasures. Find the wealthy Jewish banking family who built it.

Clue 6 Ride northwest with rings on your fingers and bells on your toes to where you may get cross if you don't find this kind of mince pie.

Clue 7 Race eastwards now to a precious stone that might well have gathered moss a few years back (when it would surely have been sterling silver). It is clearly treasure for the Chest.

Clue 8 Southwards now to where prisoner C.3.3. wrote a wild ballad. Find the multi-sided theatre where the coloured balls click.

Clue 9 Go northeast to a place where an introductory hug gets the bird and comes to a sticky end. Find the premier novelist who is buried there.

Clue 10 Finally northwest to the home of the Swan of Avon; the Treasure is the castle of his Scandinavian prince of indecision.

CLUE 6 ▲

CLUE 10 ▶

CLUE 9 ▶

S E C H R L C I S

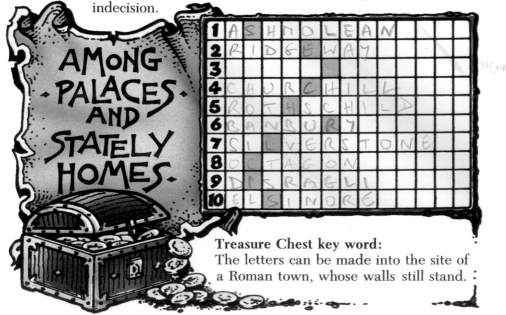

AMONG PALACES AND STATELY HOMES.

1	A	S	H	M	O	L	E	A	N				
2	R	I	D	G	E	W	A	Y					
3													
4	C	H	U	R	C	H	I	L	L				
5	R	O	T	H	S	C	H	I	L	D			
6	B	A	N	B	U	R	Y						
7	S	I	L	V	E	R	S	T	O	N	E		
8	O	C	T	A	G	O	N						
9	D	I	S	R	A	G	L	I					
10	E	L	S	I	N	O	R	E					

Treasure Chest key word:
The letters can be made into the site of a Roman town, whose walls still stand.

Armchair TREASURE HUNT-2

AMONG PALACES AND STATELY HOMES

Armchair TREASURE HUNT-3

Clue 1 Begin at a cathedral city, home of beef seasoning and union insurance, and put in the Treasure Chest the song birds of Carrow Road.

Clue 2 Southwest to where two rivers meet short of the boundary. A revolutionary campaigner for human rights stands forever before the King's House. Put his full name in the Chest.

Clue 3 North is a market town which has been bypassed, and where a treasure-seeker has beaten you to it – look for a sign in the market place and put his trade in the Chest.

Clue 4 Fly southeast for a festival where peans of praise are sung for a nationally heard composer. Find the hall where the music is ready for brewing. (Omit the definite article.)

Clue 5 Fly west to the airport city, from where eight readers annually race to Mortlake. Is the oldest place of learning where the Apostles' leader lived? Put it in the Chest anyway.

Clue 6 Take a course eastwards where the treasure in spring comes in Guineas, and you can see the Czar's son in autumn. The king illustrated started it – put his Mile in the Chest.

Clue 7 Go northeast to enter Notts (odd!) and to arrange Trent stone to make a circuit. Put it in the Chest.

Clue 8 Northwest for a man of parts (ten to be precise), who has brought gold out of Russia and America – he sounds as if it happens every day. Put him in the Treasure Chest.

Clue 9 Southwestwards for a poetic village where stands the church clock at ten to three, and is there something still for tea? (Not Brooke Bond, or not entirely). The missing nectareous gold goes in the Chest.

Clue 10 The third month and the sixth day bring you to a bridge. Cross the boundary and the drain to where Colorado's capital will fill the Chest.

CLUE 9 ▶

FAMOUS PEOPLE IN EAST ANGLIA

Treasure Chest key word:
A university writer.

▲ CLUE 1

◀ CLUE 6

TREASURE HUNT-4

Clue 1 An obvious place to begin: a lighthouse looks across to where officers train. Find an original steam engine and put its builder in the Treasure Chest.

Clue 2 West, where east is east and west is west and sharks come in between. The treasure is the animal in the woolly sanctuary.

Clue 3 Go northeast to where Mount Edgcumbe sat by the Tamar, and find by the old stewpond a medieval billing place.

Clue 4 Move south to a town with a weedkiller, where these parents left the noise for a brave new world.

Clue 5 Go northeast for the destination of Bill, Jan, Harry, and the rest – the treasure is the female companion they had in mind.

Clue 6 Southeast now to William of Orange standing on the quay – find what the Rev. H.J. Lyte penned in front of the fast falls there.

Clue 7 Northwards where St David's on the line and the museum exhibits float away, and find the oldest municipal building in England.

Clue 8 Hardy people lived at Castle Boterel to the west where a pair of blue eyes was courted. Discover the black arts of its museum.

Clue 9 Camel country, and a place where Raleigh held court: find the May Day creature who dances in the streets.

Clue 10 Over the moor to the first town past the lean, gaunt stream. Book at a place where you may have a rum encounter.

CLUE 1 ▲

CLUE 4 ▲▶

CLUE 8 ▶

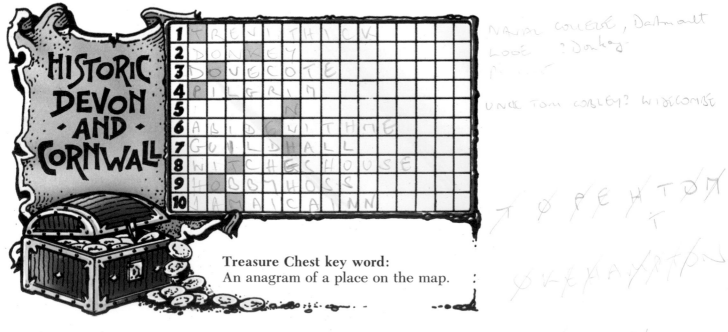

HISTORIC
DEVON
AND
CORNWALL

1	T	R	E	V	I	T	H	I	C	K				
2	D	O	N	K	E	Y								
3	D	O	V	E	C	O	T	E						
4	P	I	L	G	R	I	M							
5					N									
6	A	B	I	D	E	W	I	T	H	M	E			
7	G	U	I	L	D	H	A	L	L					
8	W	I	T	C	H	E	S	H	O	U	S	E		
9	H	O	B	B	Y	H	O	S	S					
10	J	A	M	A	I	C	A	I	N	N				

Treasure Chest key word:
An anagram of a place on the map.

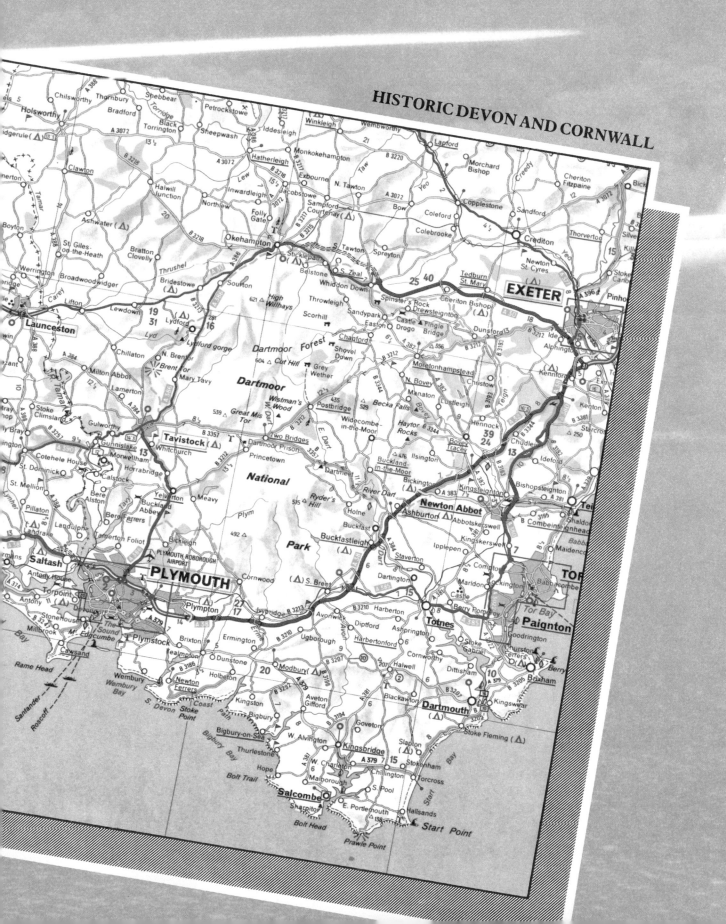

Armchair TREASURE HUNT·5

Clue 1   Start at the old Roman capital. Find the scoundrels on the mud where hooves pound. The big handicap is the treasure: it could be the archbishop's signature, or something he wears back to front.

Clue 2   Move west to the town where it's unwise to go out without headgear, and follow the river to the location illustrated, where they nominally play with Wanderers and invest with National. The name goes into the Chest.

Clue 3   Take the road east via the whalemeat buildings to the spa, and go upstream, past the place where the inhabitants should avoid stone-throwing, to the lakes. Go north to a stable home, and then walk eastwards: it sounds as if the potatoes are still too lumpy here. Put this place in the Chest.

Clue 4   Go east to Professor Higgins' friend. A wonderful heroine might leave her croquet mallet nearby – put this place in the Chest.

Clue 5   South by southwest an Italianate pile,
Built by Vanbrugh for the Earl of Carlisle,
Was revisited by fame
Under a fictional name.
Put this name in the Treasure Chest.

Clue 6   To port where a Stoker disembarked a villain who was something of a sucker. What pierced his heart should go into your Chest too!

Clue 7   Fly southwest to the village where the Rectory Bells worked in a novel way. Lock their alcoholic brother in the Chest.

Clue 8   Fly over Leeds and Bradford Airport and continue to where Scotty's captain meets a Scottish brook – and his ship goes into the Chest.

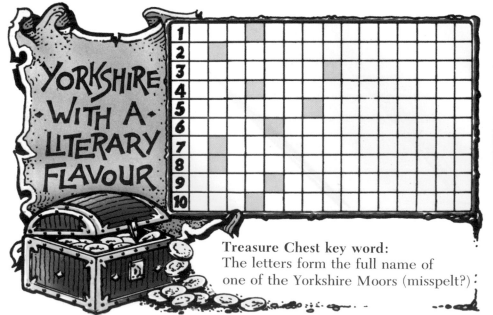

YORKSHIRE · WITH A · LITERARY FLAVOUR

Treasure Chest key word:
The letters form the full name of one of the Yorkshire Moors (misspelt)

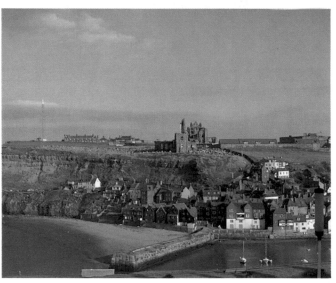

▲
▲ CLUE 1

▲ CLUE 6

◄ CLUE 2

Clue 9   West is a centre of exhibitionism – do delegates chew over the toffee? Find the common land where you might wander off the straight and narrow.

Clue 10   Go north to where not only does the Wakeman's house still stand but the hornblower still sets the watch. Find what spurred the horses to the post.

Armchair TREASURE HUNT-5

TREASURE HUNT·6

Clue 1   Start where driving has an Italian flavour and the shopping centre sounds sportingly Spanish, and find the ground on which a miss joined up and became a hit.

Clue 2   North of the happy flower, the reindeer hold a September dance. Their venue goes into the Chest.

Clue 3   In Good Queen Bess's time, another Bess made a pile far to the northeast, southeast of another seat. Hunt for the goddess in the high great chamber and put her in the Chest.

Clue 4   In a southerly direction lived a prime minister whose name went across the world. Find another born here whose influence travelled even further (two names).

Clue 5   Northwest to the gateway to the Peak, where the great cham of literature knew a green man. Find the date of the football match.

Clue 6   Further north 250 died in isolation over a box of clothes. Find on the moor the stony circle.

Clue 7   Go southwest to a collection of six, in one of which was born a chronicler of five. Drop his card (two names) into the Chest.

Clue 8   Southwards to a swinishly placed town which had an MP who owed his fame to his rivals. Find below the octagonal tower a fisherman who went bust there (two names).

Clue 9   To the southeast are the players of Belgrade. Find the man whose statesman was destroyed, and whose Messiah can be seen from ruins.

Clue 10   Up north to a home with a private theatre, but where the prams are kept under the stairs. Find what was built for Czar Nicholas (two words).

MIDLANDS MISCELLANY

Treasure Chest key word:
The letters form a well-known
Midlands rider.

78

▲ CLUE 5

◀ CLUE 1

▼ CLUE 7

Armchair TREASURE HUNT-6

MIDLANDS MISCELLANY

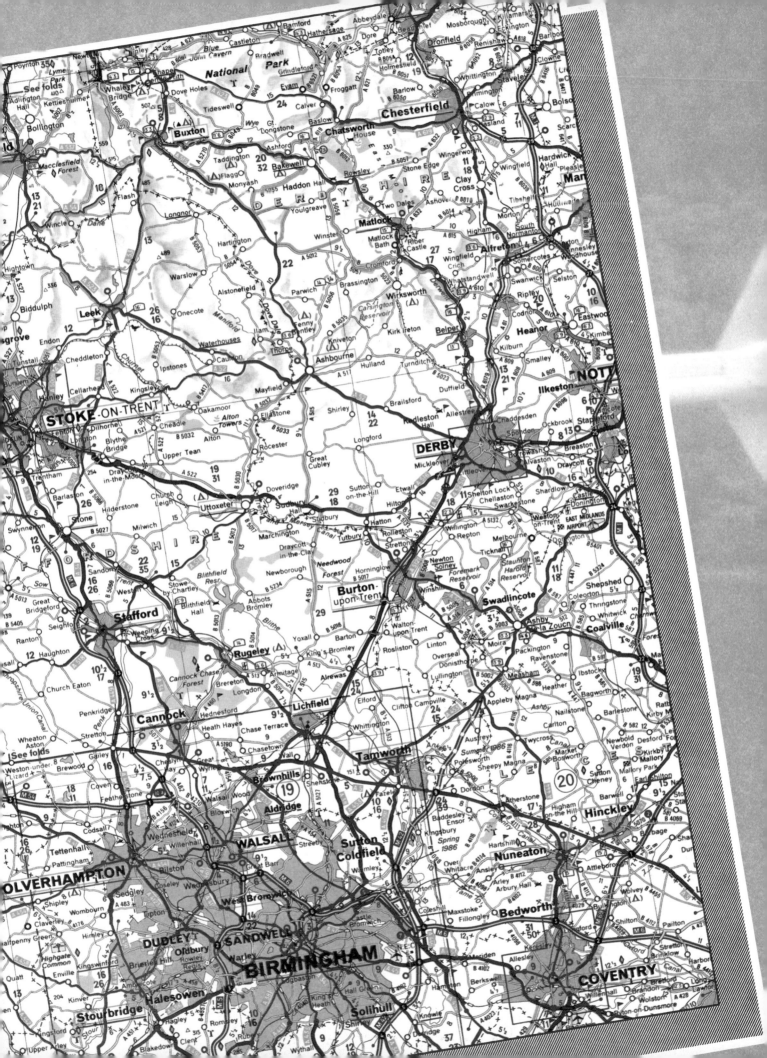

Armchair TREASURE HUNT-7

Clue 1   Begin where a mountain bird holds a mirror to the west, and there is a little railway to boot. Find the nearby village where the bird's cousin comes to an end and pop it in the Treasure Chest.

Clue 2   Among the mountains, the old man guards the bluebird's course, where an island had a wildcat camp. Capture the swallows' adversaries for the Treasure Chest.

Clue 3   Back o'Skidda, to the grave of the namesake of 2's island, and the other graves that made him famous. Find the regiment which sang their praises, and put them in the Chest.

Clue 4   By Lakeland's only lake, a lord had an idyllic vision of a king carried on a barge. Something was thrown into the lake – put its name in the Chest.

Clue 5   Quickly to the birthplace of one who roamed in solitude like a watercarrier. Find who played his mutinous neighbour in 1935 (both names).

Clue 6   Go southeast to where each August fells are for runners and falls are Cumberland and Westmorland, and find a saint whose day brings a rush to church.

Clue 7   Northeast now to the wildlife park and the earl who made the AA yellow. Put his belt into the Chest.

Clue 8   This town sounds like a film falcon's home: it was certainly the home of one whose bird-shooting sailor was very old. Put the former's first two names into the Chest.

Clue 9   To the southeast the sixth of a regal sextet was born, and a self-confessed junkie edited the local paper. Put his surname in the Chest.

Clue 10   Finally westwards to a village both far and near – where a nominal clay modeller worked. Find the name of an aquatic bird that lived on the top of a hill.

CLUE 1 ▲

CLUE 4 ▶

CLUE 9 ▼

WITH THE POETS IN LAKELAND

Treasure Chest key word:
The letters make a funny man born in the area (two names).

82

Armchair TREASURE HUNT-7

WITH THE POETS IN LAKELAND

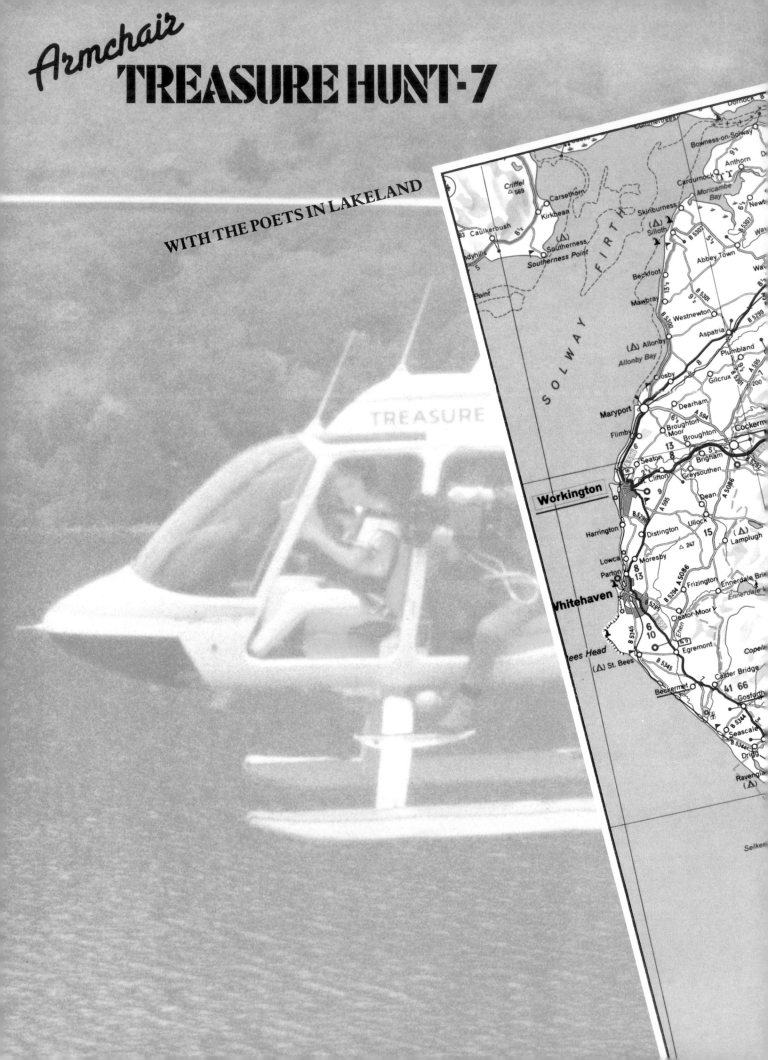

Armchair TREASURE HUNT-8

Clue 1 Begin where Trade Unionists meet each July under the old sycamore tree, and find to the south the largest dish on the heath.

Clue 2 Go north to see the lions in their bath house, and the Old Meeting House of the masons who helped build it. Find the name of their cottages.

Clue 3 Fly southeast to where coloured sands are taken away by tube and find the man whose fame is signalled by his monument here.

Clue 4 Westwards now to where King John kept Princess Eleanor prisoner for forty years and find the prophet dragged behind horses to Wareham and back.

Clue 5 Go northeast to a town where a bishop was forty times a wet and find his royal pupil in the Broadway.

Clue 6 South now to a place which has a week at sea, and a biscuit house nearby. Find the room with an Indian flavour.

Clue 7 Go northwest to where a cinema appeared by the Hall of Halle and find who painted a rainbow (surname only).

Clue 8 Now southwest to where one who is heartless in Westminster Abbey trained as an architect to name the house he built for himself.

Clue 9 Across an isle to the devil's rocks and find what must be cleared to reach no man's land from the mainland.

Clue 10 Lastly northeastwards to where saints play in a dell and find in Reginald Mitchell's Museum what supplemented a hurricane in times of stress.

CLUE 3 ▲

CLUE 9 ▼

ROCKS AND RUINS IN WESSEX

Treasure Chest key word:
The letters form the home of a hill-dweller.

▲ CLUE 8

◄ CLUE 1

ROCKS AND RUINS IN WESSEX

Armchair TREASURE HUNT-9

Clue 1   Begin where men festively tread boards and fish climb ladders, and find for the Chest the nearby waterfall.

Clue 2   Go north to island ruins in the 'loch of minnows', the remains of the stronghold of Robert II's black sheep son, and find for the Chest his lupine connection.

Clue 3   Northwest now to a well-lit point between two forts. Put into the Chest the village of the soothsayer who here found a tar-barrel too hot for him.

Clue 4   Fly south to 'the end of the pinewood' and the Highland Folk Museum. Find the barracks to which the message came to disperse.

Clue 5   Northeast now to where nominally the bridge has not replaced the ferry. Put into the Chest the visitors with the first-class fishing tackle.

Clue 6   Southwards now to where a barefoot charge came to pass and succeeded – but not for Dundee. Find the place of a long-jump record.

Clue 7   Go west to a thrice-constituted loch and find where, between the loch and the mountain of alders, a highland chief lived like an animal.

Clue 8   North now to a headquarters of monstrous activity. A cairn on the road south commemorates a fast-living man. Put his name (forename and surname) in the Chest.

Clue 9   Sail northeast now to the fair form of one who helped Prince Charlie. Put into the Chest the men of melody and drones who compete at the Northern Meeting.

Clue 10 Southeast finally to where winning the toss is enough to impress the royals gathering, and find the young treasure-hunter born here.

AMID LOCHS AND GLENS IN SCOTLAND

1												
2												
3												
4												
5												
6												
7												
8												
9												
10												

Treasure Chest key word:
The letters form a man who had a crushing effect on the region.

CLUE 8 ▲

◄ CLUE 6

CLUE 9 ►

Armchair TREASURE HUNT-9

AMID LOCHS AND GLENS IN SCOTLAND

Clue 1   Begin where the old salts come from and name the house in which Sir Charles Bunbury lost a toss as a matter of course.

Clue 2   Fly southeast to a castle with astronomical pretensions. Identify the gardening basket in the village.

Clue 3   Cross a county boundary to Jane Eyre's hero and the Royal Victoria and Bull. What did it become in a resident's expectations?

Clue 4   Go south to a village where a back rub and wash leads to a house where a preserved turbine was installed by the maker of the light that failed. Put the house in the Chest.

Clue 5   Northwest now to another house where a painter built a wall. Find the game on the card table.

Clue 6   Down south the Bonfire Boys commemorate Bloody Mary and the martyrs. Find in the Grange a forerunner (both names) of a secretive mole.

Clue 7   Go west to where horses gloriously outstayed machines. Indoors in the round is where Britannia gained currency. Find the artist responsible (surname).

Clue 8   In a northerly direction is a town where the Old Boys were fifth to win the Cup – find where the rare trees grow.

Clue 9   Northeast to the capital place illustrated. Find the connection between its imminent collapse and Eliza Doolittle.

Clue 10   Finally fly southeast to what fills the pocket in a sixpenny song and find who go on strike with the wisdom of Solomon.

CLUE 5 ▲

RACING AND WRITING IN THE SOUTH EAST

Treasure Chest key word:
The letters form one of a late queen's residences in the area (two words).

94

▲ CLUE 9

◄ CLUE 6

WIN the Armchair Treasure Hunt Competition

Armchair Treasure Hunt Prize Code

Solve the Treasure Hunt prize code by applying the following numbers to an old lady's commitment to one per cent:

2341331432104434124525114335243047

Treasure Hunt Competition – Win £1,000.

To Enter

On a separate sheet of paper list the answers to the ten Armchair Treasure Hunts (i.e., the key words) and to the prize code (eleven answers in all).

Tie-Breaker

Complete the following sentence:
   I like watching *Treasure Hunt* because . . . (maximum of fifteen words).
Send your entry (please send only solutions and not a detailed explanation) together with your till receipt as proof of purchase to: Treasure Hunt Competition, 16 Portland Square, Bristol BS2 8SJ, to arrive before March 16, 1987.

Rules

1. Competition closes March 16, 1987.
2. Employees and their families of Chatsworth Television and The Hamlyn Publishing Group and their agencies, participating bookshops and anyone connected with the competition are not eligible to enter.
3. Judges decision is final.
4. Winner will be notified and announced in *TV Times*.
5. Full rules available from promotional address. Please send a stamped addressed envelope with your request. After April 21, 1987 winner's name and correct answers also available.

£1,000 PRIZE

Organise your own Treasure Hunts!

Here are ideas and hints on how to create your own Treasure Hunts for family and friends, clubs and pubs. There are safety points, and even some samples. We discovered very quickly that many people do organise their own Hunts, and in some cases have been doing so for many, many years. The game is a good reason to be out in the open air, and it brings out the competitive spirit in all of us. Some people organise Treasure Hunts to raise money for charity, but mostly they do it because it's fun.

This sampling gives ideas of Treasure Hunts for children and adults, by day or night, on foot, by car, on a boat – even on horseback.

These general pointers apply to all Treasure Hunts:

- Safety at all times is most important.
- Be considerate of other members of the public.
- Clues should be clearly visible from public areas which are free.
- Clues should be biodegradable (e.g. paper), in case they are neither found nor collected in afterwards by the organisers, or are moved elsewhere by a member of the public.
- Trees and plants should not be disturbed or harmed.
- All property – public or private – must be respected.

• A Treasure Hunt on Foot for Children

What makes a Treasure Hunt so much fun for children? It is an imaginative game which can be played over a wide area – even in towns and cities where there is marvellous material for clues and map reading – although it is ideally suited for the countryside. The game requires quick thinking, self-control and lots of action!

Get Organised!

The first thing to do is to get organised. Even a very simple Treasure Hunt requires advance planning, from choosing the area for the Treasure Hunt and time spent on making up clues to hiding articles to collect and persuading friends or parents to help. Instructions must be carefully worded so the children are sure what to do, where to go, what time to return and understand the fact that they must stay in a team.

Like any good game, a Treasure Hunt needs rules or chaos will ensue. (Even with rules chaos can and sometimes does ensue!)

Pointers on Clues

Think of an area half a mile across with, perhaps, a school or community hall at its centre.

Ask yourself the following questions:

- Is there any part of this area you would not wish the children to explore? Clearly state this in the instructions.

- What places or landmarks within the area immediately spring to mind? (Churches, memorials, statues, museums, historic buildings, sign-posts, unusual trees, public buildings with inscriptions or notice boards.) You need at least six, or more if they are close to each other.

- Can you think of a good clue for each one?

- Is it possible to hide the next clue at each place?

- There is always a strong possibility of other people removing clues from public places, so, as an alternative, discover something on or near each landmark which can provide the answer to the question, or is there something which can be collected (ticket, leaf, signature of co-operative person)?

● Will you provide straightforward questions which name the landmarks? Or will you give clues to the landmarks and ask for information or an item to be collected at each one? Or will you provide a map with numbered points marked on it and ask for information or an item to be collected at each point? Or will you provide a map with a grid, list of grid references and information on an item to be collected at each reference?

Now you have the framework for a Treasure Hunt.

Ideas for Clues

Think the game out carefully and thoroughly and explain it in very simple words. Written instructions are useful because the children can take them along and refer to them as they play the game. At times you may wish to test them on how well they can remember instructions given verbally.

Clues can be cryptic, puzzles, quotations, in code or just imaginative, witty, daft or clever, whatever appeals. Clues obviously relate to specific places. Here are some different ideas for planning the clues:

● Write the first clue or message on the back of a child's jigsaw puzzle (about 25 pieces, preferably wooden), each word on a separate piece so that the message makes sense when the jigsaw is complete. Teams are given one piece of the appropriate puzzle (will they need the picture on the box as well?), and all the remaining pieces of each puzzle are jumbled together.

● Give a telephone number to call for instructions or to provide the next clue.

● Use map grid references – these can refer to specific places or be used to locate a word on the map, or just one letter of a word. Hence a series of grid references can spell out a message. 1:50,000 maps are best for this.

● Grid references send teams to various places. At each place is a word in a newspaper or book. A typical clue would read: 'Page 28, second paragraph, third line, tenth word'.

When all the words have been found, they make a jumbled message or instruction. Each team must have the same newspaper or book. This game can be practiced indoors.

Make a scale plan of the building and draw a grid on the plan. Use 'grid references' for places in the building where clues are hidden – under stairs, in kitchen, behind storeroom door, in washroom.

Next time, play out-of-doors with real maps. Remember street maps have grids and the grid reference principle can be used.

What Tasks are the Children able to Perform?

Always keep the tasks within the children's capabilities. Can they do simple first aid? Cope with a minor accident? Make rope ladders? Pass clear messages by telephone?

Clues can be written on the back of a jigsaw puzzle. When the puzzle is complete the message makes sense.

Send the children on a scavenger hunt for certain items or give clues leading to hidden articles which, when collected, provide the materials for the task, e.g. making a rope ladder, making a collage or picture, drawing a sketch map of their route.

How to assess the Setting

Decide what activity is suited to which part of your area, and then start to string your game together. Here is an example:

A group of children live on a housing estate quite near the sea. Between the houses and the shore lies the farm with outbuildings and two or three fields. There are two public routes to the shore: a lane and a path across the fields. On one side of the path is a wood to which you have access for collecting firewood, and beyond that a different farmer's land to which you have no access. You will naturally tend

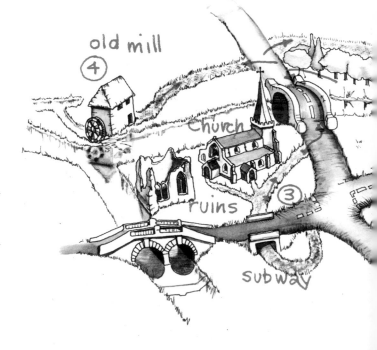

"The Quest for the Holy Grail."

old mill ④

church

ruins ③

subway

to want to use the shore – assuming this is not crowded it will be the best place for the climax of the game. What is this to be? How will you get them there? Will they follow a trail? Will they use a map? Use grid references? What food and equipment will they need? How will you obtain this? Could it be hidden and clues provided to the hiding places? Will the farmer let you use the farm buildings? Can these necessities be obtained secretly from their hiding places, without being caught by 'guards' or alerting the farm dogs?

So now you have a game which starts with a clue, involves stalking, then a trail or map, then tasks to be carried out. You will have to provide clear instructions and find a reason for all these carryings-on, i.e. a good story. Here is a real game, which has been tailored to fit existing sites and played successfully.

A Treasure Hunt – The Quest for the Holy Grail

The Grail is an aluminium jug. Each team has a compass. Three adults hide where shown on the map with squeezy bottles full of water (this was the only area really suitable for stalking). Anyone heard or seen is squirted with water (i.e., poisoned).

At each point (marked on the map with numbers) was a jumbled word.

All six words provided a clue to the Grail's hiding place.

Also at each point was a cryptic clue to the next. (Teams were not given a map – the one below is just to illustrate this account of the game.)

Each team was given one of the clues below to start off with, without the jumbled word, so each team started in a different place and travelled in a circle collecting words.

Map grid references can be used as clues.

Clues and jumbled words

1   In a glade of the forest stands a hermit's hut.   (HENDID)

2   Go 30 paces south-west to find the blasted oak.   (BENDIB)

3   Journey on across one river until you come to another river where you will find Merlin's cave.   (SUNIR)

4   There was a jolly miller once lived by the river Teme.   (DESCAR)

5   Approach with care the Lady of the Lake. She is guarded by many-headed monsters spitting poison.   (SLEVES)

6   See the banners fluttering in many-towered Camelot.   (HUCCRH)

The first group to collect and solve all the jumbled words
(SACRED VESSEL HIDDEN BEHIND CHURCH RUINS)
would be able to find the Grail.

* three adults in hiding

⑤ canoe   scarecrow   raft   pond

campsite   ⑥

hollow oak

Path

River Teme

② ①   Fisherman's Hut

* one of the hidden adults was a qualified lifesaver, and there were lifejackets

Points to Remember

● While the aim is to have fun, the safety of the children must be the primary concern. Play in teams or pairs unless it is perfectly safe for children to go alone. Although stalking, for example, is best done by individuals, there are very few areas today where a girl, especially, is safe on her own. In built-up areas or on public roads it is necessary for children to stay in teams.

● If the children have to go on or near the water, a qualified lifeguard must be present.

● Numbers participating should be limited to a maximum of about 25 to 30 children in groups of four to six.

● Boundaries are needed – define these clearly.

● Do not trespass on private property unless permission has been granted.

● If everyone is to start at once in different places have a starting signal or given time – synchronise watches first!

● Have a time limit, 'Everyone to be back here at . . . .' Are they all wearing watches? Alternatively have a finishing signal. Check that everyone is back, especially in the dark.

● Children should be warmly and comfortably dressed.

● Ensure all instructions are clearly understood before the children start to play.

Make sure children know how to use the telephone, so clues can be given this way.

● Check the game thoroughly beforehand. Is the trail fairly foolproof? Are the answers to all the clues where they should be? Do your helpers understand what they have to do and where they have to be? Do involve outside helpers (parents, local friends) to give an element of reality and/or surprise.

● Finally, adapt these or any other ideas to your own ideas and the boys' and girls' needs and situations. Make it exciting. Use a story. Have messages in code or invisible ink. Use passwords. Make it fun!

• A Car Treasure Hunt

Car Treasure Hunts are probably the most popular ones of all. They are usually organised by clubs – such as the Cirencester Car Club (one of their Treasure Hunts is included here) – pubs, groups of friends, church groups, and so on. The Rally Authorisation Department of the RAC Motor Sports Association is the authorising body for Treasure Hunts which have a set route on the public highway, if more than twelve cars take part. They have compiled some points to remember when planning your Treasure Hunt by car.

Points to Remember

● Think about where most of the competitors live, before deciding on a Finish venue miles out in the countryside, from which they will have to drive a long way home afterwards.

● When setting a route, a figure-of-eight pattern will enable the organiser to check up on the teams at about halfway, without having to travel too far from the starting point.

● How to write clues. The majority of Treasure Hunt questions revolve around extracts from the following list:
Churches: name of rector, times of services, dates on gravestones.
Pubs: name of licensee, opening times, names of beers sold, pub sign.
Post offices: name of owner, opening times, postbox collection times.
National Trust land: byelaws, any notices thereon.
Farms: name of farmer, price of manure, etc.
Roadsigns: adding up mileages, deciphering anagrams of places.
Sports venues: next match, next meeting, cost of entry.
Telephone box numbers.
Houses: number of chimneypots, colour of door, something about unusual house name.
Railway stations: train times, ticket prices.
Country houses: opening times, cost of entry.
Rivers and canals: boat names, depth of/number of locks, bathing restrictions.

● Try making anagrams or other cryptic clues out of road signs, to give directions at a junction. This is more taxing than 'turn left at the traffic lights'.

● Organise a team of Marshals to help.

● Don't leave too long a distance between clues as teams will get bored. On the other hand, the odd longer stretch will cause mild panic in the car if some five minutes or so has passed since the last clue point!

● Set a low average speed; 15 mph is quite fast enough; any higher and some cars will start breaking speed limits. With an average route length of between 30 and 35 miles, the game will last two hours.

● Don't make up the clue sheets too early, because a clue frequently disappears between the setting and the running of the event. Check the whole route the week before, preferably the day before.

● Time penalties – once the route has been finalised, the best idea is to get someone who will not be taking part to run the route beforehand to get some idea as to how long the teams will take. One point per minute late is a common figure, and easily workable. Always refer to the same timepiece, and have a back-up watch in case of malfunction.

● Teams can be of any size, but obviously a four-man (or woman) team will have double the advantage over a two-man team. There could be a handicap of a few points for overmanned teams, but make this quite clear to everybody before they enter.

● Don't start the teams together, or even at short intervals – a good few minutes should elapse between each despatch, otherwise bunching will occur on the route.

● Don't include position clue points:
– in a churchyard where a service will be disrupted (unless you have permission from the vicar);
– on a busy main road where an accident could be caused by a car stopping suddenly to catch a clue point;
– anywhere where teams will have to obstruct the passage of other traffic to answer the clue. Think about what would happen if three or four cars all arrive at the location at once.

● Marking – obtain a good selection of easy and hard questions, marked, for example, on a scale of 1 to 5 points, tailored to give a total out of 100 is possible. A thirty-mile route requires between 50 and 70 questions, but this largely depends on the features of the area the event is being run in.

● Issue teams with a sealed emergency envelope giving details of the Finish venue and perhaps a phone number to ring if they break down. If the envelope is opened, points can be deducted from the score (at least half-marks).

● Have an incentive to finish, e.g. a barbecue, or a meal at a good country pub. The price of a meal at the Finish could be included in the entry fee to stop people who get lost from going home half way through.

● When applying for authorisation through the RAD (Rally Authorisation Department) of the RAC, the organiser must sign a declaration to say that the event will comply with the standard conditions listed in the regulations. If more than twelve cars will take part in your Car Treasure Hunt, a minimum of two months' notice must be given to the RAD office. On initial application, a completed application form must be sent in, with duplicate tracings of your route, and an authorisation fee must be paid in the week or so before the event. (There is a small charge per vehicle.) Further information from: Rally Authorisation Department, RAC Motor Sports Association Limited, 31 Belgrave Square, London SW1X 8QH.

Ivan and Enid Goodfield of Cirencester have organised many car Treasure Hunts. They have a few more pointers.

Some pointers

● Car Treasure Hunts must not in any way be based on speed.

● Competitors' mileage should be noted at the beginning and end of the event and/or the start and finish time of each car, as either or both of these can be used in the event of a tie.

● The entry fee varies from event to event, but is a useful way of funding prizes. Any money not used can be donated to charity.

● 'Treasure', commonly called 'loot', is a list of items which can be collected along the way. The majority can be straightforward, but some can be cryptic. For example, 'a coin with 1771 on it is an old shilling piece – 'one shilling':   ƆNITTIHƆS

Here is one example of a complete Treasure Hunt.

CIRENCESTER CAR CLUB

TREASURE HUNT AUGUST 4TH

NAME ....
CAR NUMBER..
ENTRY FEE ....
SPEEDO READING: FINISH ....
                                       START ....
                                       TOTAL ....

THE FINISH IS AT TUNNEL HOUSE INN NR. COATES

'LOOT'

To be collected.

1 A man's black sock (left one only).
2 1 pint bottle of beer. (Non-returnable, will be given as prizes.)
3 A balloon (blown up).
4 Used postage stamp.
5 Rubber band.
6 Laurel leaf.
7 Milk bottle top.
8 Sewing thimble.
9 A marble.
10 A nail.

Please read the following notes before commencing journey.

The distance covered should be 20 miles. If your journey has taken you more miles than this *5 points per mile* will be deducted for each mile in excess.

There is a secret check along the route and it is worth *25 points.*

What is it?

MOUNT COTTAGE (organiser's old address, known to club members).

Now for clues all worth *5 points* each.

Leave the Golden Farm and drive carefully past the Police Station to the Market Place.

1 The one Centre of Cirencester that could help you that is closed? *THE TOURIST INFORMATION CENTRE*

Leave Cirencester on Glos road, A417 take 1st turn left to Daglingworth.

2 It would be essential to teach good what here? *MANNERS (MANORS SCHOOL)*

3 What can't you do at Goldings? *ALCOHOL NOT TO BE CONSUMED ON PREMISES (LOCAL OFF-LICENCE)*

Leave Daglingworth for Sapperton. Turn left at Park Corner.

4 How Many staddle stones? *FOUR*

5 Where dogs are not allowed? *EARL BATHURST PARK*

Turn right into Sapperton.

6 Not quite a Dr. Who's machine with four crowns? *TELEPHONE BOX*

7 Who was the Rector of Sapperton in 1684–1695/6? *JOSIAH GREENWOOD*

8 Who was the Rector of Sapperton in 1932–1968? *ARTHUR RUCK*

9 Name the object on the church wall. *TETHERING STAKE*

Continue on through village straight on at cross roads to Frampton Mansell.

10 It is a free house, but how many crowns? *THIRTEEN*

11 What is missing from the tap? *THE HANDLE*

12 How deep is the air valve? *3'0"*

13 How many white cones are outside the gate? *SIX*

Carry on to a cross roads.

14 Where is it not made out of chalk? *WHITE HORSE INN*

Straight on at cross roads to Rodmarton.
Straight on at next crossroads.
At the next turning right.

15 Miles to Cherrington? *2½*

Turn left and take the next turning right in Rodmarton.

16 What time is Sunday collection? *3.20 p.m.*

17 How many miles to the low bridge? *2½*

18 Rodmarton phone box number? *200X*

19 Who were the parents of Anna Maria who died January 27th, 1831? *WILLIAM AND BETTY DAY*

From Rodmarton go to Tarlton village.

20 Where do you find V.A. 1961? *THE BUS SHELTER*

21 What do you use ovum for? *POULTRY*

Leave Tarlton go towards Tetbury road turn left on main road towards Cirencester.

22 The height of the bridge is? *13'6"*

Take the next turn left for Coates.

23 Overnight stop for horses? *TREWSBURY LIVERY STABLES*

24 What did Stradlings do? *MADE THE COATES SCHOOL CLOCK*

25 Is this quite (w)right? Write it down. *THE SHEPHERDS ARMS (LICENSEE MRS. WRIGHT)*

FINISH AT TUNNEL HOUSE INN

Being a Marshal has its own rewards.

Enid and Ivan have some funny stories, each of which makes a point about Treasure Hunts.

Those who make the greatest effort to obtain the 'loot' don't necessarily win (which should encourage the less eager participants). On one Treasure Hunt, a 'loot' item was a daisy chain, with extra points for the longest chain. At the start of the game, the team in one car gathered up as many daisies as they could, and then, for the duration of the game, one woman made an enormous chain as they rode along. By the time they got to the pub, the daisy chain was so long that it had become totally entangled with the door handles and the people – and could not be removed from the car in one piece to be measured!

The temptation to be too clever sometimes fouls up competitors. An item of 'loot' was a used bus ticket. One carload saw a bus at a bus stop. They pulled up behind and an inspired participant leapt out, saying, 'I'll meet you at the next village.' That was the last they saw of him, until they got to the pub at the Finish where there was an S.O.S. message to pick him up in the village ten miles in the other direction.

Ivan concludes: 'Usually the route ends at a pub on a summer's evening for a noggin' and natter about the day's events, while the results are sorted out by the organisers.'

• *A River Treasure Hunt*

The rivers, canals and waterways of Britain are a more unusual setting for a Treasure Hunt. What could be a better combination than a Treasure Hunt and a day on the river?

Ken and Bunty Morris of Sunbury-on-Thames have organised many Treasure Hunts on the Thames, and this is an example from them of a Christmas Treasure Hunt. It is particularly interesting because it combines elements for boat crew competitors and for competitors at home. All meet at the Finish for a pub get-together (a useful enticement for any Treasure Hunt).

A Christmas Treasure Hunt on the Thames

(In aid of the Royal National Lifeboat Institution.)
This Treasure Hunt is confined to the stretch of river between Sunbury Weir and Molesey Lock. It begins at 10.30 a.m. and ends at 12.30 (boat crews) and 12 noon (home competitors).

Section I:
Open to all boat owners and crews.
Entry fee – 50p per head.

1 To solve a 'blockbuster' type set of clues, which give the boat crew the location to put ashore a 'Landing Party'.

2 The 'Landing Party' will be handed details of clues with a definite nautical flavour to be solved. The clues will lead to Father Christmas, a warming drink, and a tombola ticket, which will be the competitors' key to a share of the 'Treasure'.

3 On the way back to the Finish boat crews must solve ten cryptic clues, which refer to objects clearly visible on the river.

Section II:
A 'paper-and-pencil' competition, open to all-comers (boat crews and home competitors) who are prepared to donate £1 to the RNLI.

Here are a few examples from different parts of this ambitious Treasure Hunt.

Section I, Part I for boat crews to discover the place to put a 'Landing Party' ashore.

CHECK POINT A IS AT THE P .... L ....
I .... F .... O .... THE B .... I .... AND THE
C .... AT H .... ,

1 What 'P' can come before 'HOUSE', 'OPINION' or 'LAVATORY'?
2 What 'L' can be the arrival of an aircraft or the top of a flight of stairs?

3 What 'I' .... 'F' .... 'O' .... is the antonym of 'behind'?
4 What 'B' can come after 'TELEPHONE', 'BICYCLE' or before 'BOTTOMED'?
5 What 'I' is a hostelry, boozer, or gathering of lawyers?

. . . and so on.

Section I, Part 2: The West Route for the 'Landing Party' (There was also an East Route, to avoid congestion.)

TASK: To find Father Christmas and claim your share of the 'Treasure' by following the attached 'Straight Line Route'.

Here's how: Your route from S.P. (Start Point) to H.F.C. (Here's Father Christmas) is shown as a straight line with a few landmarks here and there, but, in fact, it does involve a great deal of twisting and turning about.

A simple map accompanied this section which showed the S.P. and thereafter all the road junctions encountered are indicated by 'X' interrupting the line. Go straight ahead. Some junctions have nautical instructions beside them. Follow these instructions in each case and carry on walking until you reach your goal – Father Christmas.

As you proceed write below the names of the roads you actually walk along and the names of the roads forming the junction at the point marked 'X'. Prizes will be awarded for correct answers.

Section II: Some Treasure Hunts are directly inspired by the television programme as is the 'paper and pencil' competition open to everyone – boat crews and those at home (who pick up the questions at an advertised location). The whole community can become involved, because competitors don't have to have boats, nor do they need to know anything about the river.

The 'hunt' is based (somewhat loosely) on Channel Four's T.V. series *Treasure Hunt*. Use your imagination as you try to win the game with resourceful and ravishing Anneka Rice, wonderful, weather-wise Wincey Willis, kindly Kenneth Kendall and the other members of the *Treasure Hunt* team.

Your 'reference library' consists of a Thames Water Authority *Launch Digest*, and a sectionalised map of the Thames between SUNBURY and READING, which are the limits of your 'hunting ground.' These and your own intelligence are all you need to compete.

The clues are inter-related, but each one is separately solvable by reference to the material provided. Points and bonus points will be awarded for the correct answers to the destination questions and prizes awarded for the four highest scores – plus some consolation prizes.

Here are some Examples of the Destination Clues and Questions:

N.B.
The non-existent helicopter flies at 90 miles an hour and is obliged by Air Traffic Control to follow the course of the river at all times.

1 (Refer to Section 3 of the map)

Imaginary Anneka's S.P. is the shortest of the three locks, on this section, which is the same width as the lock with the telephone number 0628 21650.

a Which is the S.P. lock? *CAVERSHAM*

b What is exceptional about the lock listed as the next below this one in the tables in Appendix 'F' of the *Digest*? *NOT ON THE THAMES – ON THE KENNET – NOT ALWAYS MANNED.*

2 Tell Anneka to fly downstream from the S.P. to the river crossing at the point where the river first, in this section, changes course from eastwards to northwestwards.

a What is the river crossing? *WARGRAVE FERRY*

b How far is it from the downstream limit of No. 3 Navigation District? *32.22*

. . . and so on, until . . .

7 Finally send Anneka to a place which is 26.1 miles below the bridge which is 7.3 (recurring) minutes flying time (i.e., 11 miles) above the bridge which is 2.46 miles below the fourth lock above the lock which is as wide as the height of SHIPLAKE railway bridge.

a What place? *BELLS OF OUSELEY.*

b By how many metres has Old Father Thames fallen in the course of his journey from just above the S.P. lock to this final point? *22.20*

As soon as the Morris's finish one Treasure Hunt, they start working on the next game. They use their annual Treasure Hunt to raise money for a local cause – such as the fireworks fund for the Sunbury Regatta – or for the Royal National Lifeboat Institution. On a summer Treasure Hunt they might have twenty-six boats and almost 200 competitors walking or boating. A winter hunt may involve ten boats and 100 competitors walking or boating. With their vast experience they have some hints and pointers for you.

● Safety on the water and safe handling of boats is the most important concern. Boat crews must comply with Thames Water regulations (or those that apply in your area) at all times. An experienced boater should be in charge of each boat and numbers of passengers strictly limited for safety.

● Life jackets should be worn by boaters.

● There are features peculiar to river Treasure Hunts. Competitors are limited to one or two narrow channels, so it is no secret where the others are going. Also there are few places where boat crews can land to continue the game. Because of this, most games will be limited to written answers with prizes awarded for number of points scored.

● Thorough preliminary preparation will make a better game. A number of helpers and marshals must be recruited for game day.

● C.B. radio between start points and control points is invaluable.

● A rescue boat should be present if weather is bad or crews are inexperienced.

● Passage through locks should be avoided unless there is unlimited time available.

● A scavenger hunt can be part of the overall game. The boat crews can spot clues from the boats and write them down. All the correct answers can be tied together in one final clue.

● Length no longer than two hours.

● Clues for a summer Treasure Hunt can be worked out during those long winter evenings in front of the fire. The *Treasure Hunt* T.V. programme (screened January to March) can provide inspiration!

● Always check out the clues the night before. The scene can change rapidly on the river, not to mention clues being picked up by the public. In one game a clue referred to a dove (dovecote) and a hawk (a boat). When Ken did his 'recce' by boat the night before the game, the dovecote was still there, but the 'Hawk' had sunk. When the owner heard about the role his boat had to play, he helped haul it up out of the water so at least the prow and name showed. On another occasion they had a clue which referred to 'three wheels and a fly'. They had taped a zipper on to a derelict van with only three wheels. By the next day – game day – a wrecker had towed it away! Ken also says that one or two naughty clues keep people alert.

● Donations for prizes – usually food and drink – can be obtained from local shops and pubs. John Tetlow and Gill Howie, also Sunburyites, have collaborated with Ken and Bunty on organisation for several years. They take care of this part of the Sunbury Treasure Hunt, and have always persuaded restaurant owners to include a meal for two as a prize. Others put posters up in local shops and pubs.

Although Ken and Bunty have been organising Treasure Hunts on the Thames for fifteen years, the last four years have been special for them. They have been delighted with the success of *Treasure Hunt* on television. As we have seen, they have taken on board an imaginary Anneka Rice and the team for their own Treasure Hunts on the great river which flows past their door.

Competitors return year after year.

• A Treasure Hunt in a City

By Car

Once a year an extraordinary car Treasure Hunt takes place on a summer's night in the one square mile of the ancient City of London. This Treasure Hunt is called 'Miglia Quadrato' (The Square Mile). It is recognised by the RAC and is carried out with the full, and essential, co-operation of the City of London Police.

'Miglia Quadrato' is organised by the United Hospitals and University of London Motor Club. It is planned and carried out in a highly professional way, as might be expected of an event which has occurred almost every year since 1957.

This extremely popular contest is always over-subscribed, for it requires much of the skill and supplies much of the fun of normal rallying, but with very little expense. Any roadworthy car can be used and even a Lamborghini will consume a little more than a gallon of petrol! There is a time element and sixty clues: 20 easy ones, 20 of medium difficulty, and 20 hard ones.

Each clue has a grid reference.
Examples:
320.4 809.2   Founded in ....
334.0 807.9   Years of the Diarist?

In this, the oldest part of London, competitors often become distracted by interesting features outside the very exact ten-metre limit, which is one of the features of this game. Competitors enjoy the challenge of rallying on a 1:10,000 map which makes such exact plotting possible.

Usually more than 100 teams are present at the staggered, mass start, each team consisting of up to six people in a car. Teams usually represent colleges, hospitals or motor clubs.

There is no optimum route and there are no trick questions. The Treasure Hunt starts at midnight and ends between 4.30 and 5.00 a.m., when competitors hand in their 'route cards' (answers) with a time penalty coming into effect after 5 a.m. Breakfast is then available, – pre-arranged with a restaurant – for those who have bought breakfast tickets in advance.

This is obviously a complicated Treasure Hunt in terms of advance preparation and in every other respect. Competitors return year after year and are themselves highly disciplined to play the game with the least disturbance to others.

To organise a Treasure Hunt in your city, start on a smaller scale with a daytime Treasure Hunt until you become more experienced.

Here are some notes from the organisers of 'Miglia Quadrato' for both those who plan a Treasure Hunt in a city by car and those who take part.

Pointers for Organisers

● Have a detailed knowledge of the area, including caretakers who live in. This includes understanding the area – the character of parts of the city day or night, or at certain times – the night before a market, for example, when traffic flow will be different from usual.

● The chosen city area should be largely non-residential.

● Liaise closely with the appropriate police authority.

● At all cost avoid causing offence or annoyance to any member of the public, be they resident, in transit or security officers.

● Avoid hospitals, residential areas, and busy places, for example where newspaper delivery vans will be converging.

● Clues must not be located where competitors will be tempted to stray into private areas or to park carelessly.

● A team of volunteer organisers and marshals is essential.

Pointers for Competitors

● Drive safely and carefully – and as quietly as possible.

● Park sensibly. Vehicles should not be left unattended with engines running.

● Obey all traffic signs and comply with the directions of the police.

● At night wear rubber-soled shoes and have a good 6-volt torch with fresh batteries. (Searchlights should not be used.)

● Be considerate of other road users.

● Arrive at the start with sufficient fuel for the game and the return journey home.

On Foot

On one Sunday afternoon every year for the last fifteen years, another unique event has taken place within the one square mile of the City of London – a Treasure Hunt called 'Londinium Pedo' (London on Foot). It also is organised by the United Hospitals and University of London Motor Club, with the co-operation of the City of London Police. Up to 150 teams of one or two people take part.

This is undeniably an enjoyable way to spend a Sunday afternoon, for the game is based on those hints of the past in the oldest part of London – a crumbling gravestone, a rusting plaque recalling the Fire of London, the artist's signature on a statue. It is to the often unseen oddities and antiquities of the past that the organisers lead the competitors, through tiny streets and alleys, through courtyards and passageways where it is easy to conjure up images of the past.

The object of the game is to answer the questions given on the 'route card', the location of the answer being defined by the instructions attached to each question. The answers are easy to find, some easier than others. The route itself is straightforward – simple

Comfortable shoes, a watch and a pencil are all that is required.

directions and sketch maps – and at each of six control points the competitors hand in their answers and collect fresh instructions for the next part of the route. There are six sections, with twelve clues in each, two of which are more difficult tie-breakers. A clue sheet with sketches on it and an adapted map are given for each section.

Examples:
Date of destruction by enemy action?
Whose house? (sketch on clue sheet)

To ensure that everyone has an equal chance, there is a time limit for each section of the route. (This also prevents anyone spending too long searching for an elusive clue.) The event is of a length that may easily be traversed by all competitors. There is a small entry fee to cover expenses, and competitors are required to sign an Indemnification, although this event has been remarkably free of mishap. Competitors are asked to wear comfortable shoes and to have a watch and pencil with them.

At the same time a 'Mini-Pedo' takes place with a shorter route and no stairways for those with small children or for those who feel their stamina is not up to the full event.

John and Diane Gilbert, who have helped organise many of these events, give some pointers on organising a Treasure hunt on foot in a city.

Pointers

● All information should be visible from areas to which the public have general and free access.

● Private property must be respected.

● On Sundays, places of worship should be avoided unless permission has been sought.

● Likely traffic conditions and shop opening hours must be taken into consideration.

● Consider safety when siting clues and controls. For example, do not site difficult clues on a main road, where competitors might step into the road to peruse the roofline.

● The route should not criss-cross main roads.

● Participants must compete quietly, respect plants in garden areas and comply with all police directions.

● Ability on such occasions develops with experience, so for a large Treasure Hunt start novices from the same control point. A marshal could accompany them. John suggests handing out a 'help sheet' for novices for some sections of the route ('We hate to lose competitors', he says). This might give further routing information or hints to make clue searching a little easier.

For further information about 'Londinium Pedo' or the 'Mini-Pedo' contact John and Diane Gilbert, 1 Pear Tree Dell, Letchworth, Herts., SG6 2SW, and for the 'Miglia Quadrato' John Gilbert or Paul Waters, 105 Highland Road, Bromley, Kent, BR1 4AA.

• A Treasure Hunt on Horseback

A Treasure Hunt on horseback is to most of us a novel and appealing idea. It is, of course, appropriate only for experienced horsemen and women. Horses and ponies very much enjoy this kind of competition, and seem to get as much pleasure from it as their riders. Keith Cromar of Hythe has often organised this type of game. Here are some of his tips and ideas.

Hints and Safety Pointers

● Safety and animal welfare must come first in all planning.

● Duration of the event: between three and six hours with a range of between 15 and 30 miles.

● Speed on horse/pony not likely to exceed five miles per hour.

● Route should be roughly circular, since horse boxes, trailers, etc. are normally left at the start of the ride.

● Horse boxes, trailers and horses take up a lot of space at the assembly point, so popular public car parks should be avoided. (Pedestrians and dogs can present real hazards.)

● People trained in first aid and vets must be available at short notice (on call).

● Horses/ponies obviously do not mix well with heavy traffic, so roads should be avoided. Open/forested countryside gives the best and safest ride.

● Riders always ride in small groups (in case of accident). Extra care is needed where young people are involved.

● Clues should be regularly checked by the organisers. The removal or repositioning of some signs, markers and clues by members of the public is to be expected.

● Large events need the services of a radio communications group, such as The Radio Amateurs Emergency Network called 'Raynet' – who are trained and have sophisticated equipment, which is effective over long distances. (N.B.: This is *not* CB radio.) They will set up a number of radio check points that can transmit information back to a central control point and also assist in the event of emergencies or 'lost' groups. Contact your local amateur radio club.

● Some older children could be allowed to participate, if experienced riders and accompanied by an adult.

● Assemble a team of voluntary organisers when you begin to plan the Treasure Hunt.

● Permission from the appropriate authorities (Police, Forestry Commission, etc.) will be needed, especially if more than ten riders are involved.

A New Forest Treasure Hunt

Here are more details from a typical event run in the New Forest one Easter:

Meeting place, one of the larger car parks/picnic areas in the Forest. Permission had been obtained from the Forestry Commission.

Numbers must be limited to keep the game safe and enjoyable for those who do take part. Events in the New Forest attract between 10 and 150 riders and obviously can involve quite a large team of voluntary organisers.

Pre-ride checks for safety and general condition of the horses and ponies. Local vets briefly look over each animal. Knowledgeable person examines tack. Marks given for turn-out.

Start time 10.30 a.m. Riders set off in groups at staggered times (five-minute intervals).

The Course is circular, about 12 miles, following a series of clues. Ordnance Survey maps of the New Forest are essential for each group.

Clues – about eight – are cryptic and usually relate to a gate, bridge, building or vehicle. On arrival at the correct place the next clue is collected.

Examples:
Did royalty pass this way? *Kings Passage*

To mow the grass don't forget the boat? *Long Water Lawn*

Tie-breakers are usually necessary and can take a number of different forms. One of the most popular is a 'Scavenger Hunt', while riding the route. Each group of

Children (and adults) – even horses – are keen on an Easter Egg Treasure Hunt.

riders is required to collect one item for each letter in the alphabet. (Some imagination is necessary for letters such as 'Q' and 'Z', and no excuses are accepted, if a competitor claims to have captured some strange zoological specimen, which has since escaped!)

Examples:
  'A' = Acorn
  'F' = Feather

An alternative tie-breaker could be a list of botanical items to be collected.

Winning an egg for Easter

Easter-time is a holiday-break that lends itself to something special for the younger participants. It must be noted that the not-so-young can also become somewhat involved in winning a chocolate Easter egg, as can the horses – many enjoy a small Easter egg as a special treat! The main treasure could be a large Easter egg, with many smaller eggs also to be won.

Make a number of egg symbols from paper and write on each one either an 'E' or a 'G'; they can then be spread throughout the route.

'G's should be placed in such a way as to be easily found, with 'E's fewer in number and less easily found. Symbols are pinned to trees, posts, fences, etc.

Any rider collecting three symbols to spell the word 'Egg' could claim a Creme Egg at the end of the ride. No person is permitted to claim more than two eggs.

A time limit of, say, three hours should be fixed, at which time the riders are required to give-up (if course not completed) and return to the start.

Winners are those who have either completed, or got furthest around the 'clued ride' in the shortest time, taking into account points for the pre-ride inspections and the tie-breakers.

Prizes are usually donated by a local retailer, especially a horse/pony supplies business.

Keith Cromer tells an amusing anecdote, when one of the organisers decided to tag along behind a team to see how well they coped with the route she had helped set up. The team became totally confused, and looked hopefully to the organiser, who, by then, had become completely lost herself. It was a very embarrassed organiser who eventually returned with her team long after the others had arrived at the Finish.

Keith often includes a pub stop in the game – there are some pubs in the New Forest with corrals for the horses and ponies, which facilitates this. Or the Finish can be at a pub. Many a rider has found a large head suddenly pop over his or her shoulder for a sip of Guinness (or beer, or coffee – a horse usually prefers his rider/owner's drink) at the end of a Treasure Hunt well played.

The Treasure Hunters now have their own club. For details please write to P.O. Box 600, Maldon, Essex, CM9 6EZ

Index

N.B.: Page numbers in *italic* refer to captions.

Photographic acknowledgements

Ken Andrew, Prestwick 90–1 bottom; Graham Berry, London 11 bottom, 28 top and bottom, 30–1, 32, 41 bottom; Britain on View, London 63 bottom, 67 bottom left, 71 bottom, 86 top; Channel Four Television, London/Tim Roney 26; Chatsworth Television Limited, London/Laurie Asprey 31 (all three); Chatsworth Television Limited, London/Simon Farrell front cover top and bottom right, frontispiece, 6, 8–9, 12, 14, 17, 20, 24 (all three), 29, 30 top left and right, 33 top and bottom, 34 top and bottom, 35, 36, 40, 43 bottom, 44, 44–5, 46, 46–7, 47, 48–9, 52, 54 (all four), 58–9, 59, 74–5 (top two), 86 bottom, 111, back cover; Chatsworth Television Limited, London/Dennis King 11 top, 27; Colorific Photo Library, London/Ian Bradshaw half title, 16; Hamlyn Publishing, Twickenham/André Goulancourt 58, 62–3; Michael Holford, Loughton 95 top; A. F. Kersting, London 71 top, 79 bottom, 87 top, 94–5; Tim Laming, Sheffield 75 (bottom); Limehouse Studios, London/Derek Pennell front cover left, 21, 22–3, 25, 37, 50; Frank Meyburgh, London 41 top, 43 top, 53; National Portrait Gallery, London 67 bottom right (detail of original painting), 82 (detail of original painting); The Photo Source/Colour Library International, London 63 top, 66–7, 70–1, 75 top, 78–9, 83, 90–1 top; Homer Sykes, London 79 top, 95 bottom; Bob and Sheila Tomlinson, Carlisle 75 bottom, 82–3, 91; ZEFA, London 87 bottom; Richard McLaren/DPA, London 15.

Acknowledgements

The publishers express their appreciation to the following for their information and help: the Treasure Hunt for children on pages 99–104, adapted from *Wide Games* by Ruth Black, the Girl Guides Association, 1984, used with permission; Chris Norman of the Rally Authorisation Department, the RAC Motor Sports Association Limited for information on pages 102–103; Keith Cromar; Diane and John Gilbert; Ivan and Enid Goodfield; Ken and Bunty Morris.

Drawings on pages 100, 101, 102, 104, 107, 108, 110 by James Hughes.